A WORLD OF MYTHS AND LEGENDS

ANCIENT STORIES FOR TODAY
RETOLD BY STEVEN ZORN

D1248367

Ottenheimer
PUBLISHERS

ACKNOWLEDGMENTS

I am grateful to Deborah Thornton Pendleton for starting me off on the right track, and to Julie Williams for keeping me there. I also wish to thank Charles Powell for his insight, patience, and dining room table, all of which were essential to this book's completion.

CONTENTS

THE MEANING OF MYTH

Introduction

IT'S A HUMAN NEED to try to make sense out of the world around us. Sometimes the simplest, most childlike questions are the most profound: How did we get here? Why are we here? What happens when we die? These aren't idle queries. The need to find answers lies at the core of our humanity. These are the questions that, in a spiritual sense, form the basis of our religions; in a physical sense, they fuel our science.

The tales that we call myths provide consoling and, at times, reassuring explanations about fundamental questions of creation, death, love, the cycles of nature, and just about everything else. All cultures have grappled with the same large issues in their quest to understand the world. Today we may be finding somewhat different answers, but the questions that compel us remain the same. Over thousands of years their importance has never diminished. The variety of explanations that have accumulated—in the form of myths and legends—tells a rich and intriguing story about our world and its people.

Many of these tales of imagination show fascinating similarities from culture to culture. Some of these links arose from cultural exchange—when two different societies brush against one another, some beliefs are bound to rub off. The best-known example of this is the mythology of ancient Greece and Rome. When the Roman Empire expanded, it adopted a majority of the Greek gods. But when Latin poets such as Ovid wrote down the Greek myths, they gave the Greek deities Latin names.

Nonetheless, ideas and stories would not cross cultures unless they carried some thread of truth and satisfied similar needs. In every myth is a kernel of truth about the world and our relation to it. Even in cultures that have had no contact with one another, many similarities in their myths are still apparent. Whether a person lives in northern Canada or central Africa, he or she will still witness birth and death, interact with heroes and tricksters, experience the changing seasons and fickle weather. The individual will still be part of a social order, feel the same range of emotions, and ultimately look around and wonder *why?*

The human brain is a complex organ, home to an inscrutable imagination. Each of us has a brain, and on a very basic level—the physiological one—our brains do not differ very much. We make sense of the world in more or less the same way, and so our stories of explanation resemble one another.

Many scholars have devoted their lives to studying mythology in minute detail, and many complex theories about the world's cultures have been formed. But that's not the goal of this book. Rather, it is to present some of the world's legends simply as stories to be read for pleasure. In this book you will encounter a wide variety of myths from around the world—stories of creation and nature, love and adventure, humor and happiness, death and destruction. You may enjoy each of these compelling tales independently or compare them and look for patterns and parallels between cultures. Either way, they will delight and surprise you, for these ancient stories still have universal appeal to the human heart and imagination.

1

CREATION

HOW DID THE WORLD BEGIN? How do we humans fit into the grand scheme of things? These are perhaps the most fundamental questions of all time as people try to comprehend their big and baffling world.

Despite the earth's great size and wild abundance, people have long observed and experienced some order in the world. The first sprouts of springtime, the birth of a baby, the morning sunrise—such ordinary but spectacular events display the universe's creative essence. Amid the danger and challenge of ancient people's lives sprang perfect creations, apparently gifts of the gods. But it didn't take early societies long to figure out that these uplifting acts of creation were only half the picture. Each is balanced by a destructive or negating force. For every springtime there comes an autumn, for every birth there is a death, and each day is followed by night. Add to that the birth process itself—painful, bloody, traumatic—and it's not hard to imagine that the creation of something so vast as the universe was viewed as equally tumultuous.

People created elaborate myths to explain the creation of the world. Though these myths differ from culture to culture, each reflects to some degree a sense of the turbulence and conflict that ancient peoples observed in the world around them. Before the creation, all was chaos. Then, according to most myths, cosmic forces clashed and the victor imposed order on the elements of creation, thus forming the world as we know it.

ORDER OUT OF CHAOS *Greek*

Before there were gods, monsters ruled. And before there were monsters, there was an endless, swirling sea called Chaos.

Out of the turbulent depths of Chaos came the earth, whom the Greeks called Gaia. She wasn't beautiful or green or glimmering with oceans. That would come later. First she was a featureless mass, ripe with possibilities, surrounded by disarray—and she was utterly alone.

Then something peculiar happened, though no one is sure quite how. Out of Chaos, or perhaps out of Gaia herself, sprang Eros, the god of love and desire. He was born long before the other gods—even before the creation of darkness and light. Love was one of the first elements of creation, and desire was the force that drove the creation of all things to come.

Eros spurred Gaia to produce Uranus, or the Heavens, to envelop and embrace her. She also adorned herself with mountains and oceans. The union of Gaia and Uranus produced a race of giants, called Titans. Some of the Titans were truly beautiful and benevolent; others were ugly and cruel. After the Titans, Gaia gave birth to three other giants, called Cyclopes. Each Cyclops had a single enormous eye in the middle of its forehead. The Cyclopes possessed incredible brute strength, yet they were also superb craftsmen and had godlike powers.

Worst of all were the last of Gaia and Uranus' children, the Hecatoncheires—three beasts huge beyond belief, each having fifty heads and one hundred hands. Gaia loved these creatures as she loved all of her children. But Uranus, who was jealous of the attention Gaia paid to their offspring, rejected these monsters completely. As they were born, Uranus forced them back into Gaia's womb so that they should never see the light of day.

But the giants kept growing inside Gaia and her pain became unbearable. Something had to be done! She plotted her revenge on Uranus. First, she produced some iron, from which she forged a large, serrated sickle. Then she called her children, the Titans, to her.

"I am not a woman of violence," she said solemnly, "but your father's savagery demands that I respond in kind. My injuries must be avenged through the blood of my husband, your father. Who among you will help me carry out this sorry labor?"

The Titans trembled. Truly, Uranus' cruelty was extreme, but who had the courage to fight such a powerful adversary, to take up arms against his own father?

"I shall help you, Mother," declared Cronus, the youngest and brashest of the Titans. "Father has shown no love to us, and his cruelty to you must be repaid."

Very pleased with her son, Gaia handed him the sickle.

With weapon in hand, Cronus waited patiently. Then one night, as Uranus came to pay a visit on Gaia, Cronus leapt out and struck Uranus with the sickle, injuring him. Blood from the wound sank into the earth and eventually grew into haglike spirits of vengeance, known as the Erinyes, or the Furies. These creatures stalk the earth and hound people who kill wrongly. Uranus' blood also produced a race of giant warriors and ash-tree nymphs.

Flesh from Uranus' wound floated for a long time in the sea. As the ocean churned over it, white foam formed. Within the seafoam grew a beautiful young goddess. On her frothy carpet she drifted among the islands, eventually coming to rest on Cyprus. There she emerged as Aphrodite, the goddess of love.

The defeated Uranus went off to live in solitude, and Cronus now ruled the Titans. He chained the reborn Hecatoncheires and the Cyclopes, his hundred-handed and one-eyed brothers, in Tartarus, the underworld. Then he married his sister, Rhea. Uranus cursed Cronus and the rest of the Titans, declaring that their days were numbered, and prophesied that Cronus' own offspring would destroy him. Cronus took the warning very seriously. A crime as terrible as his could not go unpunished, but he would do everything in his power to prevent the prophecy from coming true.

Rhea bore Cronus five children: Hestia, Demeter, Hera, Hades, and Poseidon. But Cronus, fearing the prophecy, would not allow them to survive. He kept a constant vigil over his wife and swallowed his children as soon as they were born. Rhea's despair was unrelenting.

"Mother Gaia, Father Uranus," Rhea pleaded, "my husband has consumed each of our children. I know his crime is great, but I am the one who is being punished for it. I am soon to have another baby. Please help find a way for me to have it in secret, so that Cronus cannot devour it and so that it may live and prosper."

"Your words are touching and tragic," replied Gaia. "It is true that you bear the brunt of your husband's punishment. But he acts out of caution, not cruelty. It has been decreed that one of his children will bring an end to his reign, and an end to the Titans."

"But fate cannot be avoided," interrupted Uranus, "and it isn't right that you should be deprived of children. Yes, dear Rhea, our daughter, we will help you to keep your baby away from Cronus' clutches. Just beware the terrible consequences of your actions."

Just as Rhea was about to give birth, Uranus managed to distract Cronus, and Gaia whisked Rhea off to the isle of Crete. There Rhea had a baby boy, whom she named Zeus. She then took the boy to a deep and inaccessible cavern, where she weaned and raised him.

Rhea couldn't keep her son a secret forever, though, and when Cronus found out about him, he demanded to see his son so that he might devour him. Rhea wrapped a huge rock in swaddling clothes and presented it to Cronus, who swallowed it in one gulp, never realizing he had been duped.

The years went by. Zeus grew stronger and Cronus grew older. At last Zeus saw his chance to deal fate's blow. Disguised as a cup-bearer, he presented Cronus with a vile potion. Cronus consumed the potion and promptly vomited the rock and the children he had consumed, all of them unscathed despite their ordeal. Defeated and outnumbered, Cronus retreated to Tartarus.

Together with his brother and sister gods, Zeus began the fight to establish the home of the gods on Mount Olympus. To accomplish this goal, the gods first had to defeat the giant Titans. The battle, fiery and fierce, raged for ten years. Neither the Titans nor the gods seemed to be making any progress, but the Titans fought to keep what was theirs, and the gods fought for what they were fated to win.

Finally, Zeus traveled to Tartarus and released the Titans' monstrous kin: the Cyclopes and the Hecatoncheires, whom the Titans had chained in Tartarus at the beginning of their reign. Out of gratitude, the monsters swore allegiance to Zeus and fought against the Titans.

The Cyclopes, who were master craftsmen, forged powerful weapons for the gods. To Poseidon they gave a deadly trident; to Hades, a helmet of invisibility. Zeus was awarded the most powerful weapon of all, the thunderbolt. Zeus flung these blazing bolts relentlessly at the Titans, until the earth shook and the sky was lit as if with fire. The gods were also aided by Prometheus and his brother Epimetheus, two rebellious Titans who believed that the way of the gods was superior to the way of the Titans.

Finally the fierce Titans were defeated. The gods, along with Prometheus and Epimetheus, then took their rightful place on Olympus, and the Titans were banished to Tartarus and guarded by the Hecatoncheires. A special punishment was reserved for Atlas, the Titan who had led the battle against the gods. He was condemned forever to bear the huge weight of the heavens upon his shoulders.

LIFE OUT OF DEATH *Norse*

Between an icy region called Niflheim and a land of fire called Muspellheim flowed a steaming river. The steam condensed to form clouds, which in turn became the first living creature, a giant named Ymir. Any creature formed from such primitive, opposing forces as heat and cold is bound to be in a bad mood most of the time, and that was true of the frost giant. Caught between unbearable heat and chilling cold, he was foul-tempered and cranky, though at first it really did not matter much because he was all alone.

Life was dull, so Ymir spent a good part of his time sleeping. While he slept, he sweated, and from his left armpit came a male and a female giant. Another frost giant came from his sweating feet. This was the beginning of the race of frost giants.

Meanwhile, out of the condensing steam emerged a huge cow, named Audumla, which produced four rivers of milk to feed the hungry giants. Audumla sustained herself by licking the salty ice. One day, while lapping at a particularly large ice chunk, her warm tongue exposed a tuft of hair. The next day she uncovered the rest of the head. By the third day, her tongue had melted enough ice to reveal the fully formed body of Buri. Unlike the frost giants, Buri was handsome and even-tempered. Though he wasn't a god, he had special powers.

Through magical means, Buri had a son, named Bur, who eventually married Bestla, one of Ymir's daughters. Bestla gave birth to three sons, Odin, Vili, and Ve, each one a god. The gods were very different from the frost giants. Where the gods were creative, orderly, and civilized, the giants were argumentative, violent, and wild. It wasn't long before the gods grew tired of the giants' wicked ways.

"Ymir and his kind wallow in this awful place," said Odin to his brothers. "Ymir has the power to create a more hospitable land, and yet he sees no reason to improve it. He rejects all our offers and ideas for fashioning a world of greater comfort."

"He has been here for so long that it is all he knows," said Vili. "For him this land of fire and ice has become a comfort."

"It has poisoned his disposition and tainted his race," added Ve. "Misery feeds on misery. As more time passes, the ranks of vile giants will continue to swell. If we are to make changes, we must make them soon, for the giants are powerful adversaries and the numbers are already in their favor."

"But they're disorganized and prone to fighting among themselves," Odin reminded them. "If we were to kill Ymir, we could easily vanquish the rest of the race."

So the brothers decided to kill the king of the frost giants. While Ymir slept, Odin slew him with a sword. From each stab gushed an unstoppable torrent of gore, which drowned all but two of the giants and settled to form vast seas.

The brothers dismembered Ymir's body. They used his eyebrows to delineate a region that they called Midgard, positioned between Niflheim and Muspellheim. Within the boundaries of Midgard, the gods fashioned the earth. They formed Ymir's flesh and his bones into the land and the mountain ranges. His teeth became boulders, and his hair became plants.

Then the brothers hoisted up Ymir's skull and from it created the dome of the heavens. His brains became the clouds. They stole sparks from Muspellheim and scattered them into the heavens, where they became stars. The largest embers became the sun and the moon. At first the heavens had no order, but then the gods positioned the stars and determined how often the sun and the moon were to appear.

The two surviving giants were banished to a very dark and uninviting region outside of Midgard called Jotunheim, where their numbers increased. Living in these dreary surroundings, the giants grew to hate the light. When Odin set the sun and moon in the sky, the giants grew furious. They sent two gigantic wolves into the heavens to devour the brilliant orbs. Each month one of the wolves manages to take bites out of the moon, which fortunately escapes long enough to grow back to its full roundness again.

The wolf that pursues the sun rarely catches it. But on those rare occasions when he does manage to get the sun in his mouth, its heat causes him to quickly drop it. But the gods know that one day, the wolves will succeed in their mission, and the giants will escape from Jotunheim for the ultimate battle. The evidence is in the sky above as it is in the ground below: Every earthquake is a reminder that the giant Ymir, from whose flesh and bones the earth was crafted, is not totally dead, and his descendants are destined to gain the upper hand.

After creating earth and the heavens, the gods built for themselves a celestial abode called Asgard, and filled it with beautiful palaces made of gold, silver, and jewels. The most luxurious of these palaces is Valhalla, the home of Odin. His servants are armored, warlike virgins called Valkyries, whose main duty is to view earthly battles and decide who has died a heroic death, thus earning a place beside Odin in Valhalla. The Valkyries travel between Midgard and Asgard through a rainbow "bridge" called Bifrost. As the Valkyries ride through the skies on their horses, their gleaming armor flashes and sparkles, producing wondrous lights in the northern sky.

With the giants banished to Jotunheim, Odin and the other gods were free to create the world of wonder they envisioned. The earth they created was a tranquil and lovely place, but aside from trees, grasses, and other plants, it was devoid of life. As Odin, Vili, and Ve contemplated the creation of people and debated what they should look like, maggots began to gather on what was left of Ymir's body. From these maggots the gods fashioned a human prototype—a race of dwarves. But the gods soon realized that the dwarves weren't the solution.

"The dwarves are smart, and they're hard workers," said Vili, "but they still have such plodding, nearsighted ways. Besides, they are always hungry. They seem better suited to life in the earth than upon it."

"Not only that," added Ve, "they are also all male."

"I like the dwarves," said Odin, "but I agree they're not the final answer to what we are looking for. Let us give them their own region within the earth, while we continue to work on our plan for humans. In the meantime, as they die, we will create new replacements so that their race will be perpetuated."

Time went on and the challenge of human creation continued. As the gods strolled the earth they debated the size that humans should be.

"They should be tall like the giants," declared Ve.

"That sounds like trouble," countered Vili. "Giants are hard to control and Midgard cannot support many of them. They will wreck the place. Better we should make humans small, like the dwarves."

"Too tiny!" Ve asserted. "Life would be too difficult for them. We've crafted nature on such a grand scale, they would get swallowed up by it!"

Just then they came upon a dead ash and a dead elm tree that had decomposed.

"Look at those tree trunks," said Odin. "Once they were small seeds and then small saplings. Then they grew to be enormous trees. Now they are dead, and nature's forces have broken their trunks into the size we see them today. Let nature decide the size of humans for us. We will use these trees as our template."

So the gods turned the ash tree into a man, whom they named Aske. From the elm tree they created a woman, and called her Embla. After giving Aske and Embla life, Odin gave each one a soul. Vili gave them the power of intellect and reason. Ve gave them emotions, creativity, and speech. And from Embla and Aske sprang all of humankind.

FROM CELESTIAL WATERS *Egyptian*

The universe began as a void called Nun—disordered, wet, and endless. As fate would have it, a small portion of Nun came together and formed Atum-Ra, the first of the gods, who was like a giant hill in the middle of swirling chaos. Atum-Ra spat, creating Shu, the god of wind, and his twin sister, Tefnut, the goddess of dew and moisture. Shu and Tefnut made love, and their union created another set of twins, Geb, the earth god, and Nut, the goddess of the sky. From Atum-Ra's tears sprang humans, who populated the earth under his watchful eye.

To Atum-Ra's displeasure, Nut and Geb were so fond of each other that they remained locked in a tight embrace. He directed Shu to force them apart, which he did; thus, the wind separated the earth and the sky. Nut appears as a giant cow. On her back she carries Atum-Ra as he travels across the sky with the fiery orb of the sun. The stars adorn her belly.

Before their separation, Nut became pregnant with Geb's children. Atum-Ra was furious. "You will not give birth to any child in any month of any year!" he told her.

Despondent over her curse, Nut appealed to Thoth, the ibis-headed god of writing, logic, and judgment.

"Thoth," cried Nut, "you are among the wisest of the gods. With your intellect and your magic, do you see any hope for me and my unborn?"

"This is a predicament, fair Nut," replied Thoth. "I can't undo Atum-Ra's decree, but we may be able to work around it."

Thoth pondered the problem for some time. Soon a plan began to form in his mind. He visited the moon and showed him a deck of cards, which he had just invented, and taught him how to play games with it. Once the moon caught on, Thoth challenged him to a bet.

"Let's make this more interesting," said Thoth. "If I win the next game, you must give me some of your light. Just a bit of light—this is a friendly game, after all."

"And if I win?" asked the moon.

"I will name this game after you."

"I accept your challenge," said the moon.

The two friends played many rounds over several hours. Thoth made several concessions to the moon, even agreeing to update the calendar to make the moon's job a little easier. Eventually Thoth won what he had come for. Saying good-bye to the moon, he paid a visit to Nut, carrying a large chest with him.

"What's in it?" asked Nut.

"The answer to your problems," declared Thoth. "Take a look."

Nut opened the lid a hair's width and was struck by a blinding flash of light. Blinking her eyes, she was speechless.

"I . . . I don't understand. What is this and how can this help me?"

"This, my dear Nut," grinned Thoth, "is five days' worth of light. Atum-Ra decreed that no child of yours will be born on any day of any month. But if we add five days to the year, and don't assign them to any month, then you can bear your children without breaking Atum-Ra's law."

"You are as brilliant as the light inside that chest!" declared Nut joyously.

In this way, Thoth expanded the calendar from 360 days to 365.

During these five days Nut gave birth to four powerful gods: Osiris, Isis, Set, and Nephthys. Osiris, tall, dark-featured, and beautiful, became the god of agriculture and the principle deity. His sister Isis then became his wife. She was the mother goddess, responsible for crop growth and fertility.

Set delivered himself by bursting through his mother's abdomen on the third day. He was the god of darkness and destruction, the evil brother. He ruled over the night and desert animals. His sister Nephthys also became his wife. She was the goddess of dusk, and was both friend and foe to Isis and Osiris.

Together, these powerful gods balanced good and evil, light and dark, creation and destruction.

MARDUK SHAPES THE WORLD *Babylonian*

Apsu, the sky god, and his wife, Tiamat, the goddess of chaos, had many children together. Their first union resulted in the old gods, who were wise and peaceful. But their second union produced the young gods, who were immature and disobedient.

One day, Apsu and Tiamat were arguing about their horde of unmanageable children.

"The young gods are too unruly and boisterous!" complained Apsu. "All they do is laugh and carry on. I cannot get a moment's rest. I say we destroy them."

"What!" said Tiamat. "Destroy our own children? They are willful and just need some understanding."

Apsu was unconvinced and became determined to destroy the young gods to attain peace. But Ea, the all-knowing young god, learned of Apsu's plan and killed his father before he could carry it out. Tiamat was enraged at the murder of her husband, but she swallowed her anger and spared her young children.

Things went well for a while, but soon the young gods grew noisy again. Ea created the four winds, which bellowed and blew and annoyed Tiamat. The howling winds and raging storms pained Tiamat and her older children. Meanwhile, Ea and his wife had a son, Marduk, born full-grown and magnificent. Marduk had four eyes, and nothing could escape his scrutiny. He had four ears to catch every sound. He was taller, stronger, and more handsome than all the gods. On his head he wore ten crowns, and when he spoke flames shot from his lips.

"My son, my son! He is like the sun itself, the light of heaven!" marveled Ea.

Tiamat and her older children weren't quite so impressed. Taunted by noise and assaulted by storms and winds, they were in no mood to deal with an upstart young hero.

"Mother," one of the older children said to Tiamat, "you let Ea murder Apsu, you allow their raucousness to disturb our peace, and now you endure the pain they are causing with their tempests. The unchallenged power of Marduk does not bode well for us either. It is time to avenge the name of our father and destroy our younger brothers and sisters."

"I suppose you are right. My patience is wearing thin." replied Tiamat. "There seems no end to their nuisance. The time has come to be rid of them."

Tiamat created an army of eleven monsters to unleash against the young gods. She fashioned monstrous serpents whose veins coursed with venom rather than blood. She made tremendous dragons who could kill with a terrifying glance. She created a mad dog, a man-scorpion, a storm giant, and other fearless enemies of the gods. Then she chose the god Kingu from among her older children to lead the battle.

When Ea learned of Tiamat's forces, he knew that even though he had defeated Apsu, he couldn't hope to vanquish Kingu and his army of monsters. The only god with the courage and strength to claim victory was Marduk. The young gods called Marduk before them and asked him to help.

"I will fight against the destroying forces and win our victory," said Marduk, "but if I do this, you must declare me the supreme ruler. You must put your destiny in my hands. From now on my word, not yours, will become law and all must obey."

The young gods had little choice but to accept Marduk's terms, and the terms seemed reasonable. A lavish banquet was prepared to crown Marduk and fortify him for the battle. They gave him kingly robes and a scepter. They declared that his word would be law, that whatever he willed would come to pass. Next they gave him invincible weapons: a bow, winds of all velocities and directions, a hurricane, lightning, a mace, a net, and a tempest-chariot drawn by four powerful, wind-swift steeds.

Marduk was ready. He followed the sound of Tiamat's rage and found her shouting orders to Kingu and his soldiers. At the first glimpse of Marduk, Kingu and his forces quaked with terror. So fearsome was the hero that Kingu's soldiers couldn't even look upon him. Petrified with fear, all Kingu could do was turn tail and flee. His monstrous army followed close behind. Now Marduk and Tiamat stood alone.

"Why do you wage war so on your own children?" bellowed Marduk, unleashing a flooding downpour. "Do you not love them? Can anything be as evil as what you propose to do? You promote a coward such as Kingu to do your pathetic bidding, dishonoring yourself and your dead husband. Stand alone and we will fight, one to one."

Tiamat shook with fear but stepped forward to engage him in battle, muttering spells and curses. Marduk spread his net to capture her and then let loose a devastating wind to stun her. Tiamat opened her mouth to engulf the wind, but it was too powerful, too swift. It raced into her mouth, filled her belly, and continued streaming into her. Bloated and stretched by the wind, unable to close her mouth, Tiamat stood helpless. Marduk pulled an arrow from his quiver, placed it on his bow, and released it. The arrow pierced her stomach and split her heart. As the wind raced out of her gut, she lay down, dead.

Marduk rounded up the monsters and Kingu, bound them in his net, and then imprisoned them. Then he returned to Tiamat and separated her body, placing half of it above to form the sky and the heavens and the other half below to form the earth. He made clouds from her saliva, mountains from her skull. He divided out the year and the phases of the moon, and gave order to the whole universe. He honored the young gods by decorating the heavens with starry constellations in their images.

To honor Marduk, the young gods in turn built a godly kingdom on earth, called Babylon, a magnificent temple city. Then they asked Marduk to create servants so that they might live a life of ease in Babylon. Ea suggested that these servants be made from the body of Kingu. Marduk agreed. He called for Kingu, slaughtered him, and fashioned a race of servants from his blood.

"Let it be known and remembered," declared Marduk, "that this new race will be called 'man' and his purpose is to serve the gods and give us pleasure."

Those were Marduk's words, and no god can change them.

BUMBA'S ILLNESS *Bantu/African*

In the beginning Bumba was alone in the darkness. He awoke one day in terrible pain, his stomach churning like the water that surrounded him. He was queasy and weak and felt like dying. An awful sensation came upon him. It grew and it grew. Suddenly, he retched and vomited up the sun.

Light spread everywhere, and with it came warmth. It dried up the edges of the endless, churning sea and revealed reefs and sandy shorelines. But there was no life.

Still queasy, Bumba vomited up the moon and the stars, which separated day from night. But the pain wouldn't go away. He retched again and out of his stomach came the first living creatures: the leopard, Koy Bumba; the eagle, Pongo Bumba; the crocodile, Ganda Bumba; the tortoise, Kono Bumba; the little fish, Yo; the lightning, Tsetse; the heron, Nyanyi Bumba; the goat, Budi; and a beetle with no name.

From these creatures sprang all the other animals that crawl on the earth, fly over it, or swim in its water. The heron created all the birds, except the kite. From the crocodile came serpents and iguanas. The serpents then created grasshoppers, and the iguana made hornless animals. Animals with horns came from Budi, the goat. Yo, the fish, made all the fish in all the oceans and lakes. The beetle made all the insects, except white ants. But as hard as she tried, Tsetse, the lightning, couldn't create anything. Every attempt was a dismal failure and even resulted in the destruction of something that someone else had made. Bumba grew tired of Tsetse's mischief, so he banished her to the sky. Even so, she sometimes sneaks down to earth and pay a visit.

Bumba was still queasy, and he disgorged a race of men and women. But the world was not yet finished. Out of Bumba came three brothers, Nyonye Ngana, Chonganda, and Chedi Bumba.

The brothers told Bumba that they would finish creating the world. Nyonye Ngana, the oldest, made white ants, but the effort killed him. To honor their creator, the ants dig into the earth to bring up soil to bury him.

Chonganda created the first plants, which gave rise to all the trees and shrubs and grasses and flowers that grace the earth. But the youngest son, Chedi Bumba, was at a loss for something new to create. Finally, he managed to produce the small bird that we call the kite.

At last Bumba was feeling well again, so he paid a visit to the earth. He noticed that since Tsetse had been banished, the people of the earth were without fire. He showed them that fire lives in every tree, and he taught them how to capture it for their use. Then, before leaving, he said to the people, "Behold these wonders. They belong to you."

IZANAGI AND IZANAMI *Japanese*

The universe was like a giant egg, with an unshaped, earthly yolk surrounded by a fluid heaven. A shoot suddenly grew between heaven and earth, and from this shoot sprang a race of nature gods. These gods produced generation after generation of new gods. In the seventh generation came Izanagi and Izanami. Like their ancestors, they lived in heaven.

One day while standing on the floating bridge of heaven and looking toward the nebulous earthly waters, Izanami pondered aloud, "I wonder what's down there and whether it's worth visiting?"

Her brother was equally curious. "Here, let me reach down with my spear and see what comes up." Leaning as far as he could, he dipped his jeweled spear into the depths. As he raised it, mud dripped from it and immediately congealed, becoming an island.

"Smart trick, brother," said Izanami. "Let us go to live on that island. We can make it beautiful."

The two deities went to the island, where they erected a wide pillar. Izanami walked around it in one direction, while her brother went the other way. When they met, Izanami said, "Oh, look at that handsome man! Let us marry."

Izanagi was not pleased. "You are a woman. It is I who should have spoken first. It's improper for you to propose marriage to me. Let's go around the pillar and try this again."

So the two walked around the pillar as before, and this time when they met, Izanagi was the first to speak. "Oh, look at that beautiful woman! Let us marry." The two were wed, and they learned to make love by watching a pair of birds. Their first off-spring was a leech-child, a bloated and shapeless baby that was the result of Izanami's error of proposing first. This leech-child was set adrift on a bed of reeds and was never thought of again.

The couple's other children were much more auspicious. The

first of these were the eight islands of Japan. Next they produced more islands, along with trees, wind, oceans, rivers, mountains, and other natural features. Each of these earthly features also contained gods to watch over them. Izanami and Izanagi's last-born was the god of fire, but during its birth, the infant burned Izanami with a fever and illness, killing her. Izanami crawled down to Yomi, the grim underworld, to spend eternity.

"Wretched child who kills his mother!" shouted Izanagi at the infant fire. He picked up the fire-baby and cut off its head. Three dragon gods sprang from its blood, and three mountains grew from its body. The dragon gods scattered to the mountains, to the valleys, and to the water, where they ruled over rain, snow, and other weather elements.

Izanagi, missing his wife, pursued her to Yomi. "Dear sister, dear wife," said Izanagi, "I have come to rescue you from this place of gloom. Our work is not yet finished."

"Good husband," said Izanami, weeping and cloaked in the darkness of her cavern, "if only you had come sooner, for now it is too late. I've eaten food of the underworld, and must remain here forever. Don't linger in this awful place, and don't pursue me or look upon me, but return to the upper regions and the beautiful world we created together."

But Izanagi couldn't bear to leave his wife in Yomi without one final glimpse of her. Torn between Izanami's wish to be left alone and his desire to be with her, he finally decided that he could not live without seeing her again. Pulling a comb from his hair, he lit one of the teeth and carried it as a torch into Izanami's cave. His once-beautiful wife was now hideous and revolting. She lay in her bed with maggots swarming over her body. Eight thunder gods who had been born from parts of her rotting flesh sat upon her.

"You have humiliated me!" shrieked Izanami. In his horror Izanagi fled and was chased by the ugly hags of Yomi. As the hags closed in on him, Izanagi tore off his headdress and threw it on the ground. It immediately turned into a bunch of grapes. When the hags stopped to eat the grapes, Izanagi sprinted ahead. His furious wife then dispatched the thunder gods and Yomi's soldiers to pursue Izanagi. Izanami herself led the chase. By now Izanagi was close to the yawning exit of Yomi. As he ascended he happened upon a peach tree. Picking three peaches, he threw them at the mob racing behind him, driving them off. Reaching the mouth of the cave and emerging into daylight, Izanagi sealed the exit with a boulder. Izanami and Izanagi then shouted at each other from opposite sides of the rock.

"You are no longer my wife!" yelled Izanagi. "You've become a monstrous thing to behold and you've become wicked as well."

"I no longer wish to be married to you," replied Izanami. "But you must pay for the humiliation you have caused me. Here are my terms: Since the powers of creation that we both shared are now yours alone, I swear to destroy one thousand people of the world each day."

"I accept your terms," retorted Izanagi. "I will just create fifteen hundred people each day." With nothing else left to be said, he turned his back and walked away.

Feeling defiled from his passage in Yomi, Izanagi set about purifying himself in a river. Every article of clothing that he flung down as he undressed became a different god. Even the dirt he carried back from Yomi on his shoes became two evil gods. And as he dove into the water, the splash he made created an assortment of sea gods.

Still disgusted with what he had seen in Yomi, Izanagi took out his left eye and washed it. It became the goddess of the sun, Amaterasu, whose beauty and radiance shone above anything else yet created. Then Izanagi washed his right eye, and it became the moon god, Tsukiyomi. The moon god was only half as beautiful as his sister, Amaterasu, but he was still a great joy to behold. Then Izanagi blew his nose, producing the storm god, Susano-o. Izanagi assigned lovely Amaterasu and her handsome brother Tsukiyomi to the sky so that their radiance could be enjoyed by all creatures. He sent the impetuous Susano-o to live in the sea, where his antics still trouble the world at times.

THE GREAT MAUI *Polynesian*

The great trickster god Maui was responsible for bringing about many changes in the world. But his beginnings were not very encouraging. He was born prematurely, the fifth son of a mortal woman named Taranga.

"No good can come of this weak infant," said his mother. "He'll surely not survive, so I'd better be rid of him now before I grow to love him too much." Taranga cut off the topknot of her hair, placed tiny Maui on it, and put him in the sea. There he floated, festooned with seaweed and surrounded by jellyfish, until the sea god took notice and rescued him.

Maui began to grow under the sea god's care. Soon he was strong enough to leave and seek out his birth mother. He finally found her at a festival. His brothers were there, too, watching the dancers. Maui joined them, and when Taranga came to claim her sons, she counted one extra. "You are not my son," said Taranga to Maui.

"But I am, Mother," replied the boy. Taranga didn't believe him until he told her about being set adrift on her hair.

Taranga hugged the boy and accepted him back into her family. "I'll call you Maui-Tikitiki-a-Taranga, Maui of Taranga's Topknot," she declared.

Growing up, Maui showed more ambition and curiosity than his brothers. One day he secretly followed Taranga on one of her daily visits to the underworld. There he met his father, the god Rangi, who blessed him and gave him special powers. But in his blessings, his father forgot to recite a certain prayer, and Maui's days became numbered.

Maui grew quickly to manhood. He had magical powers and knew no fear. One day, his grandmother handed him a jawbone and said, "You will find this bone very useful throughout your days.

Its creative energy will enhance your own powers and enable you to do extraordinary things."

Not long after receiving the jawbone, Maui's brothers invited him to go on a fishing trip. While his brothers used ordinary hooks and caught ordinary fish, Maui used an elaborate and beautiful hook made from a sliver of the jawbone.

Out in their canoe, the brothers laughed and fished and fooled around. "Why aren't you fishing?" they asked Maui.

"I was just getting ready to," Maui replied. He tied his line to his fancy hook, then punched himself in the nose and used some of the blood for bait. His brothers thought the whole thing was a little bizarre, but they waited to see what would happen. Maui cast his line, waited a little while, and then began pulling it up. He pulled and he pulled.

"You've hooked a big one!" one of his brothers exclaimed.

"Don't let it get away!" another cheered him on.

Maui kept pulling and soon it was clear that what he had fished up was not a fish at all, but an island! The little canoe was now completely grounded on a perfectly flat, dry surface. The brothers were amazed. They thought they were on the back of a huge fish, and so they began to cut it and hack at it with their knives and poles, dividing the island in two and creating mountains, valleys, and rivers. Today that island is called New Zealand.

OLD MAN COYOTE CREATES THE EARTH
Crow/Native American

At first there was only Water—Water and Old Man Coyote, that is. Or so it seemed.

One day, Old Man Coyote saw some ducks paddling by.

"My brothers," he said to them, "you are ducks, so you like this sort of thing, but frankly, I find all this water tiresome. Surely there must be something more solid holding it up."

"Actually, Old Man Coyote, we wouldn't mind having some-place dry to go to every now and then either," replied one of the ducks, paddling in circles.

"Then I have an idea. Why don't you dive down to the bottom of this water and bring up a little of whatever's down there? Then I can shape it into a pretty decent place to stand, I'm sure."

The duck plunged into the depths and was gone a very long time. Just as Old Man Coyote thought he must have drowned, up he popped, gasping for air. "There is something solid down there, but I could not get it," panted the duck.

"Let me try," said a larger duck, and down he went. He was gone for an even longer time, but eventually he surfaced, gasping and coughing.

"Any luck?" asked Old Man Coyote.

"Brother, I have brought you some stuff from the bottom of the water. Here it is, stuck to my webbed feet."

"Good work," said Old Man Coyote. "This little bit of mud is enough to start with." He then blew on the mud and it grew and grew. It became the solid earth.

"How impressive," quacked the ducks.

Old Man Coyote spread the world westward, making it just as big as he could. In no time, life began appearing. A coyote howled in the distance. Then Old Man Coyote picked up some more mud and fashioned all the other animals and people. Then he brought them to life.

He taught the people how to build tepees and how to make tools and use them. He showed them how fire can be used for heat and light and for cooking. All the animals and people went their separate ways, but everywhere they went the land looked the same. So Old Man Coyote fashioned mountains to add variety, created rivers and streams to carry water into the vast, dry middle expanses of the land, and placed the stars in the sky. At last, Old Man Coyote was satisfied with his creation.

2

HEROES, MONSTERS, AND TRICKSTERS

HUMAN SUBORDINATION TO ALL-POWERFUL GODS is played out in many epic tales of quests and labors. Heroes and heroines are often sent on quests because they have offended the gods in some way, or they seek out quests in an attempt to become godlike themselves. Sometimes the gods test humans or use them as earthly tools to enact their will. These are stories of magic, adventure, and danger, driven by strong personalities and populated by colorful characters and fantastic monsters.

The appeal of these tales goes far beyond the mere adventure story. Reading them, we feel compelled to identify with the heroes and their predicaments. Even when the heroes are more than human, their problems are human indeed. Hercules is forced into a job he doesn't like. Sigurd, despite his bravery and sincerity, can't escape his grim destiny. Within each of these tales are important human lessons. They teach that no matter who we are and what powers we may possess, the world is bigger and more powerful than we. We must accept our fate and fight our own demons with utmost heroism. Sometimes we'll succeed, sometimes we won't.

The trickster is a special kind of hero. Generally, tricksters take no one's side but their own. Their motivation is never the cause of humankind; they are merely trying to protect their own selfish interests. Tricksters have very healthy egos—they love to demonstrate their cleverness and skill by showing off or pulling pranks. The results of their actions may be either good or bad. Luckily, though, the results are usually beneficial. Trickster tales often helped bewildered ancient people to explain why some things are the way they are.

Monsters, on the other hand, personify the unknown—the unspeakable dangers that lurk in the world. They symbolize an unambiguous, universal enemy that heroes and heroines can pit themselves against. These stories of monsters and those who fight them show us that the dangers that lie just beyond our experience can sometimes be conquered and tamed, thereby making the world that much more civilized.

HERACLES' GREAT LABORS *Greek/Roman*

Heracles, the mortal son of Zeus, was his father's pride and joy. Zeus' wife, Hera, was not particularly fond of Heracles, because the infant was the result of one of Zeus' many adulterous affairs.

"One day my baby boy is destined to become a god!" declared Zeus, bursting with pride.

"Never!" said Hera. "Mortal he was born, and mortal he will remain."

"Hera! My dear wife," said Zeus, his anger rising, "I am the most powerful god. My word is law. You forget that far too often."

"If Heracles is to become a god, shouldn't he prove himself worthy?" asked Hera.

"Of course," said Zeus. "What do you propose?"

"I suggest we give him twelve labors to perform. If he can successfully complete them, then he will prove his worth, and I won't say another word on the subject."

"Fine," responded Zeus with great confidence.

"Fine," repeated Hera, venomously.

Hera was a woman who hedged her bets. When Heracles was about a year old, she sent two serpents into his crib, hoping they would crush and devour the infant. But the baby Heracles awoke just in time to strangle the snakes with his bare hands. It was then clear to the gods that Heracles was no ordinary infant. Heracles' reputation as the strongest man on earth had taken root.

Growing up, Heracles had the best tutors, but his physical prowess soon outstripped his mental abilities. He was prone to tantrums, and as a young man, he accidentally killed his music teacher by braining him with a lute.

As a young man, Heracles rescued Thebes from the Minyan king, who was extorting money from the Thebans. For his heroism, he won the hand of Megara, the Theban princess. Though they had three children, their marriage was ill-fated. Hera afflicted Heracles with madness and made him believe that his wife and children were his enemies. In a frenzy, he slaughtered Megara and his children. When he later regained his sanity, he was racked with grief and horrified beyond measure. Desperate to cleanse himself of his crime, he consulted the Delphic oracle, whose priestesses could see the future and divine the will of the gods. A priestess told him he must offer himself in servitude to Eurystheus, king of Mycenae. It was the will of the gods.

Heracles, willing to do anything to atone, humbly presented himself before King Eurystheus.

"I have journeyed far for a singular purpose, King Eurystheus," said Heracles. "I have come to cleanse my name of a terrible wrong that I committed."

"What is it you want of me?" asked the king.

"I come to offer myself as your servant. Only then will my sin be pardoned."

"What is your name?"

"Heracles."

Eurystheus was pleased to have the strongest man in the world volunteer his services. Never realizing that he himself was under Hera's power, Eurystheus devised a dozen labors. Each was considered impossible for Heracles to perform.

Heracles' first labor was to kill an enormous lion that was laying waste to the valley of Nemea. No ordinary animal, the Nemean Lion's claws were razor-sharp and its teeth could bite through iron. Heracles came upon the beast as it returned to its cave, bloody and sleepy after a kill. His arrows, which ordinarily could fly straight through a tree trunk, merely glanced off the lion's hide. So Heracles thrust his sword into the lion with all his might, but the sword bent as if it were lead. Meanwhile, the lion stopped in its tracks and began to clean its paws. Next, Heracles tried his club. It crashed down with a mighty thwack upon the lion's skull, but the beast merely shook its head and went about its business.

Heracles was getting riled. He was a man who loved to fight, and this was getting him nowhere. In his rage he jumped on the lion and grabbed it around the neck with his bare hands. Man and beast tumbled on the ground. Bloodied by a swipe from the lion's claws, Heracles refused to let go. With a final crunch, he broke the Nemean Lion's neck, killing the creature. He carried his trophy back to Eurystheus.

Eurystheus was terrified by the sight of the dead lion, proof of Heracles' immense strength. To protect himself from this super-human, the king ordered Heracles to remain outside the city gates and communicate with him only through messengers. Meanwhile, Eurystheus had an underground brass chamber built so he could hide whenever he heard that Heracles was in the vicinity.

Heracles' second labor was far more dangerous. Eurystheus commanded him to kill the Lernaean Hydra, a nine-headed mon-ster that lived in a swamp near Lerna. Its doglike body had nine snakelike necks, each neck ending with a tooth-filled head. If this were not bad enough, its breath was deadly poison, and one of its heads was immortal.

Realizing that this labor might require more than brute force, Heracles prayed to Athena, the goddess of wisdom, for advice. Fire would be the secret to success, Athena suggested. Accompanied by his nephew, Iolaus, Heracles arrived at the Lernaen swamp. First he shot flaming arrows at the hydra, but it was no use. The mon-ster closed in. Its nine mouths snapped and salivated; its long necks snaked around Heracles' arms and torso. Holding his breath, Heracles cut off three of the heads with a single blow. Instantly, six heads grew back.

Meanwhile, Hera, watching from Mount Olympus, the home of the gods, dispatched a giant crab to snap at Heracles' legs, but he crushed its skull with his foot. Even though the crab failed in its mission, Hera rewarded its efforts by placing it in the sky, as the constellation Cancer.

Heracles called for Iolaus to bring a torch. Now, as Heracles sliced off each head, Iolaus burned the stump so no head could grow back. Soon, all that remained of the Hydra was the hissing, spitting, immortal head, which Heracles buried under a boulder. Successful in his labor, he returned to Eurystheus.

From the safety of his brass chamber, Eurystheus then assigned Heracles several more labors that required him to kill or capture monsters and remarkable beasts. These creatures included a sacred stag with bronze hooves and golden antlers; a wild boar; a rampaging bull; a terrible flock of man-eating birds with armor-piercing beaks; four flesh-eating mares; the three-headed hound that guarded the underworld; and a herd of cattle guarded by a monster with three bodies and six arms.

Not content with the elimination of this gallery of monsters, Eurystheus, still under Hera's power, devised even more labors for Heracles. With humiliation in mind, he ordered him to clean the filthy stables of King Augeas. The king owned several thousand cattle and sheep but for many years had neglected to maintain their stables and pastures. Heracles swore he could clean them in one day and accepted the task. He then diverted the courses of two rivers to flow through the stables and cleanse them.

Another of Heracles' labors depended more on sensitivity than the brute force he was famed for. Eurystheus had a daughter, Admete, who coveted the golden girdle worn by Hippolyte, queen of the Amazons. Eurystheus ordered Heracles to fetch it. But this labor promised to be difficult. The Amazons were a race of ferocious women warriors who excelled at riding and at combat with the sword and the bow and arrow. They often even cut off one of their breasts to allow them to better draw the bow. They fought fiercely and conquered many armies and cities. As a result they amassed a huge trove of gold and jewels. They wore helmets and clothing made of tough hides, and carried shields shaped like the half-moon. The Amazons had no use for men, except for two days each year, when they would mate with a neighboring tribe. The male children from these couplings would be left with the male tribe, killed, or crippled and kept as servants.

Recruiting a brave band of volunteers, Heracles sailed to Cappadocia, the land of the Amazons on the river Thermodon.

His band arrived, fully armed, and was met at the port by Queen Hippolyte herself. Heracles stepped off the ship alone to meet her, signaling to his crew to stay where they were. Hippolyte, captivated by such a fine specimen of manhood, invited Heracles to dine with her. Heracles then took her aboard his ship, where, as a token of affection, Hippolyte handed him her girdle.

This was not the sort of labor that Hera had in mind, and she was furious. Disguised as an Amazon, she spread the rumor that the Amazon queen was being abducted. In no time the beach was covered with Amazons in battle gear, preparing to overrun the ship. Heracles, believing he had been betrayed by Hippolyte, killed her and most of the Amazons before returning to Eurystheus with the girdle.

One of Heracles' final labors also became one of his most complicated, requiring strength, courage, cunning, and ingenuity. Eurystheus commanded him to collect the golden apples that grew in a wonderful garden that Gaia, the earth goddess, had given to Hera and Zeus as a wedding gift. The garden was now home to the Hesperides and their father, Atlas, who was condemned to bear the weight of the heavens upon his shoulders.

This labor concealed many challenges for Heracles. First, to find out where the garden was, he had to wrestle Nereus, a god who could change his shape and who knew the garden's location. When Heracles grabbed Nereus, the god transformed himself into all manner of beasts, but Heracles hung on tight. Finally, Nereus relented and told Heracles where he could find the garden. He also advised him to have someone else pluck the apples for him once he found them.

On his way to the garden, Heracles found his path blocked by Antaeus, a colossal bandit who was a son of Gaia. The two burly figures began to fight. Heracles was amazed to find that every time he knocked Antaeus to the ground, Antaeus would rise stronger than before. Not a moment too soon he realized that this son of the earth must be gaining strength from his mother. Finally, Heracles lifted Antaeus high over his head, thus removing all of the giant's contact with the earth, and choked him to death.

Heracles passed the rock where Prometheus, who had stolen fire from the gods, was chained and condemned to have his innards forever torn by an eagle. Heracles managed to kill the eagle and win Prometheus' freedom.

When he arrived at the garden of the Hesperides, Heracles found that it was guarded by a mighty serpent, which he slew. Atlas was his next hurdle.

"What is your purpose here?" Atlas asked.

"I am known as the strongest man on earth," replied Heracles, "and I wonder whether I can support the heavens on my shoulders, as you do on yours."

"You have come here to relieve me of my burden?" asked Atlas, amazed at Heracles' offer.

"Just for a moment, to see if I can succeed at such a marvelous task. But I can only do so if you collect for me the golden apples from the tree of the Hesperides."

Atlas, who would have done anything to get a moment's relief from his burden, gladly agreed to pick the apples. Carefully he placed the heavens onto Heracles' shoulders, went to collect the fruit, and a short time later returned with the apples. But seeing Heracles bearing the heavens, he said, "This great duty suits you, Heracles. If you hold the heavens for a few months more, I'll bring these apples myself to Eurystheus."

"That's fine," said Heracles, "but can you take the heavens back for one moment longer so that I may cushion my shoulders?"

"Fair enough," said Atlas, placing the apples on the ground and once again receiving the heavens on his shoulders.

"Thanks for your help," said Heracles, laughing as he scooped up the apples and dashed off to present them to Eurystheus.

Having completed his labors to Hera's satisfaction, Heracles made peace with the queen of the gods. He went on to have many more adventures, and when it came time for him to die, he instead joined the immortals on Mount Olympus, fulfilling Zeus' prophesy.

THOR'S DILEMMA *Norse*

Armed with his mighty hammer, Thor, the god of thunder, was the invincible keeper of universal order. But one time, he lost his weapon and had to pay a humiliating price.

One morning in Asgard, the home of the gods, Thor couldn't find his hammer. He called Loki, a trickster giant whom the gods tolerated because he occasionally proved useful.

"You're so disorganized, Thor," teased Loki. "How could you be so absent minded?"

"This is serious, Loki," answered Thor. "It isn't possible that I could have misplaced the hammer, jeopardizing the safety of Asgard. I think it was stolen as I slept, and I want you to find the culprit. I suspect it was a giant."

"The only giant capable of such an act is Thrym. He is a master thief, though he is otherwise fairly dim. I'll pay him a visit and see what he says."

Loki went to Jotunheim, the realm of the giants, and called on Thrym.

"My good friend Loki!" exclaimed Thrym. "Did the gods tire of you and send you back here?"

"Nothing like that," replied Loki. "I've come to ask a favor. I want to play a trick on Thor by stealing his hammer, and I know that you're the expert in these matters. So, tell me, master thief, if you were to steal it, how would you go about it?"

"Hah, hah!" laughed Thrym. "That's an easy one. I would distract the guards of Bifrost, cross the rainbow bridge, and swipe Thor's hammer while he wasn't looking."

"Brilliant!" exclaimed Loki. "But once you had it, where would you hide it?"

"Simple, I'd bury it eight miles deep in the earth, over by—" Thrym stopped abruptly and glared at Loki. "You know I have the hammer!" he shouted. "You were sent here by Thor. I'll never tell you where it is!"

"Would you be willing to trade for it?" coaxed Loki.

"Trade? There is nothing I would want that is equal to the hammer . . . except maybe one thing."

"And what is that, pray tell me."

"To wed Freya, Asgard's most beautiful goddess."

Loki returned to Asgard, announced to the gods that he had found the hammer thief, and relayed the ransom demand.

"Ridiculous!" shrieked the enchanting Freya. "I will not be traded like common chattel. It's disgusting. Besides, my husband, Frey, would never allow it."

"Dearest," cooed Frey, "the hammer is Asgard's greatest treasure. We must retrieve it somehow."

"Absolutely *not*. I *will not* do it!" screamed Freya.

"I had anticipated this," said Loki, "and I have formulated a plan. If we can dress a god in wedding garb and present him as Freya, we can win back the hammer."

"What god among us would suffer the humiliation of dressing in women's clothes?" laughed Thor.

"Well, Thor, it *is* your hammer," said Loki.

Before Thor knew what was happening, he was being fitted for a bridal veil.

Thor, dressed in a wedding gown and accompanied by Loki, attended the wedding banquet. Seated at the table next to Thrym, Thor consumed eight salmon, an entire ox, and all the lingonberry dainties. He washed it all down with three casks of mead.

"Quite an appetite for a lady!" exclaimed Thrym.

"With good reason!" explained Loki. "She was so excited about wedding you that she hasn't eaten in eight full days."

Flattered beyond belief, Thrym turned to Freya to gaze into her beautiful eyes. Instead, he saw Thor's flashing pupils and he jumped back, startled.

Loki was quick to reassure him. "For the last eight days the poor dear couldn't sleep from eager anticipation of this day."

At last it was time for the ceremony. Loki reminded Thrym of his deal. Thrym ordered the hammer brought out and placed before the bride-to-be. No sooner had the hammer been set down than Thor grabbed it in his mighty fist, threw off his veil, and slew Thrym and all the other giants attending the affair.

Satisfied, Thor and Loki returned to Asgard. Thor swore never to let his hammer out of his sight again.

SIGURD'S ADVENTURES *Norse*

Sigmund was a great warrior who could not be beaten on the battlefield. He alone was able to pull a charmed sword from the trunk of a tree—a sword placed there by the god Odin. With this sword, Sigmund was invincible. It brought him great victory and renown. But one day Odin decided that Sigmund's time had come. In the heat of battle, Sigmund wielded his sword and it broke in two. Mortally wounded on the battlefield, leaving behind his pregnant wife, Sigmund requested that the pieces of the sword be passed to his unborn son, Sigurd.

Sigurd was destined to become a great hero. As a young man, Sigurd was visited by Odin, disguised as an old man, who told him that he would become invincible if he forged the sword back together. After Sigurd joined the two pieces, he struck the blade on an anvil and was amazed to see it cut right through the anvil. "Now," he thought, "I am ready for adventure."

"Adventure, my boy?" said his mentor, Regin. "There is no greater adventure than to kill the dragon, Fafnir, and take the hoard of gold and the magic ring he guards. But beware—the treasures are cursed and will bring misery to anyone who owns them."

"I have no interest in treasure, especially if it is cursed," said Sigurd, "but dragon slaying sounds heroic to me. I must go!" So off they went to battle Fafnir.

On their way, they discussed the best strategies.

"His breath is fire, so I cannot approach him from the front," said Sigurd. "And his scaly tail could crush me like an insect. What do you recommend?"

"Like most creatures, he is most vulnerable in his belly," replied Regin. "If I were you, I would dig a pit and hide in it. Then, when Fafnir crawls over it, raise your sword and you can easily slit his gut open."

The plan seemed reasonable enough. Arriving at the opening of Fafnir's lair, which lay in the depths of a deep forest, Regin went to hide while Sigurd dug the pit. Suddenly Sigurd looked up from his labors to see an old man watching him.

"Sigurd," said the old man, "what foolish plan is this? This pit you dig now will become your grave, for you will drown in Fafnir's blood unless you also dig channels to drain the blood away."

Before Sigurd could even speak, the old man vanished. Sigurd then realized that he had been visited by Odin, the chief creator god.

Sigurd had no sooner finished digging the drainage trenches when he began to feel the earth trembling and to hear a low, vibrating rumble. At first almost inaudible, it began to gain in intensity. Fafnir was coming. Sigurd quickly jumped into the pit and took up his sword. Earth from the edges of the freshly dug hole tumbled onto his feet. Looking up, he saw flocks of birds taking to the sky. He heard the forest animals shrieking and cackling as they fled to safety. All the while, the sound of Fafnir's footfalls grew louder and louder. *Thrum, thrum, thrum!*

Then he began to smell the stench of the beast and to feel the air grow hotter as Fafnir exhaled his fiery fumes. Sigurd had never known such terror. Sure enough, Fafnir approached the edge of the pit. Looking up from below, Sigurd could first see flames, then the monster's lower jaw. Putrid saliva dripped down upon Sigurd as Fafnir passed over him. Next, he saw the leathery throat. Then the scaly chest. The dragon's enormous body nearly blocked out all the light in Sigurd's pit, but in the dimness he could make out the pale and vulnerable belly. Mustering all his strength and courage, he plunged his sword into it and split the dragon open. Instantly Sigurd was deluged in blood, completely submerged. But soon the trenches he had dug carried the gore away. The dragon's death roar was deafening. Then, suddenly, all was still.

Fafnir's body blocked the opening of the pit, so Sigurd crawled through one of the drainage trenches into the light of day. Soon all the animals and birds returned to the forest. And, seeing it was safe, Regin came out of hiding.

"Nicely done!" said Regin. "Now that I have led you on your first adventure, could you do me a favor? To commemorate this great occasion and to toast your courage, I would like to eat the roasted heart of Fafnir the dragon."

"It is an unusual request, but if that is what you wish, we will do so," replied Sigurd, who was covered from head to toe with Fafnir's blood.

Despite the gore, the dragon's blood was magical. It rendered Sigurd's mortal skin invincible. But one small spot on his back remained vulnerable because the blood had not touched it.

As Sigurd roasted the heart, he licked the dragon's blood from his lips. This gave him the power to understand the speech of birds.

"Be warned," the birds told him, "Regin is treacherous. He means to kill you and take the credit for killing Fafnir. He wants the treasure, and he wants to steal your honor. He had hoped that you would drown in Fafnir's blood. Now he has to raise a knife against you. Watch your back. Also, eat the heart yourself. It will give you wisdom."

Sure enough, Sigurd turned around just in time to see Regin coming at him with a knife. Sigurd killed Regin and then ate Fafnir's heart. After he had rested, the birds told him of Brynhild, one of Odin's beautiful daughters. "She saved a man whom Odin had doomed," explained the birds, "so her father punished her by putting her into an endless sleep, surrounded by a ring of fire until a fearless man can rescue her. Now she is completely mortal, but her beauty remains divine. We can show you where to find her."

"Now that is a treasure that interests me!" declared Sigurd. "Show me the way." He left the hoard of gold behind but kept the magic ring as a souvenir, forgetting about the curse it carried.

He followed the birds through the dark forest until they came upon a clearing. In the center was a ring of fire, and within that lay the beautiful, sleeping Brynhild. Sigurd, unafraid and virtually invulnerable, rode right through the fire and kissed Brynhild's lips, awakening her. The two immediately fell deeply in love, and Sigurd vowed to marry her. "But first I must go and prepare a place for my beloved wife to live," said Sigurd. "I shall leave you here, protected by the ring of fire, but I swear I will return to you, Brynhild. Here is my ring as a token of my love and my promise." And he gave her the magical ring.

Sigurd's journey for a place to call home took him to Burgundy. There the king's daughter, Gudrun, fell in love with him, but all Sigurd ever talked about was Brynhild. This made fair Gudrun extremely jealous. She asked her mother, Queen Grimhild, who was skilled in the art of magic, what to do.

"Here is a potion, Gudrun," said Queen Grimhild. "Give it to Sigurd and not only will he fall deeply in love with you, but he will forget all about Brynhild."

To Gudrun's delight, the potion worked, and in no time Gudrun and Sigurd were married.

Gudrun had a cowardly but kindly brother, Gunnar, who became a close friend of Sigurd's. His mother, Queen Grimhild, wanted the best for her son. Who would be a more noble wife for her son than the daughter of Odin, the now legendary Brynhild? But Grimhild knew that her son wasn't up to the task of rescuing the maiden from the ring of fire. Through her magical meddling, Grimhild transformed Sigurd into Gunnar's double, and Gunnar persuaded Sigurd to woo Brynhild on his behalf.

Since Sigurd had been gone for over a year, Brynhild accepted the proposal from the false Gunnar, even though her love for Sigurd hadn't faded. "It appears that my true love has abandoned me," she said. "Since you were brave enough to come to rescue me from this ring of fire, I will marry you." They exchanged rings, and Sigurd, disguised as Gunnar, once again regained his magic ring.

Soon after Sigurd and Brynhild arrived in Burgundy, the real Gunnar stepped in. Sigurd gave the ring to Gudrun to make up for his long absence.

Gunnar and Brynhild were quickly wed. After the wedding Brynhild saw Sigurd for the first time since he rescued her. She grew intensely jealous of Gudrun. Gudrun, likewise, became jealous of Brynhild, upon learning that she was Sigurd's true love.

Even so, Gunnar was now Brynhild's husband, and she would let no ill be spoken of him.

The two women constantly tried to outdo each other. One day, while bathing in a river, Gudrun implied that Gunnar had been a coward his whole life.

"If he were such a coward," countered Brynhild, "then he could not have rescued me from the ring of fire. That is the most courageous act that ever was."

"Courageous, yes," agreed Gudrun, "but it was not Gunnar who performed the act. It was really Sigurd, my brave and honorable husband who wooed you that second time, as a favor to the cowardly Gunnar."

"Lies!" declared Brynhild.

"Then look here," Gudrun sneered, holding out her hand. "Is not this the ring that you gave Gunnar? But that was really Sigurd you gave it to, who in turn gave it to me—the woman he loves."

The evidence was undeniable, and Brynhild swore revenge. She fanned the flames of her husband's jealousy by telling Gunnar that Sigurd, in his guise, had slept with her for three days when he rescued her. "I know I was won by deception," said Brynhild, "but now my honor, and yours as well, is at stake because of Sigurd's treacherous act. You must kill him."

"But we swore to never raise our swords against each other," replied Gunnar.

"Then find someone to do it for you."

Gunnar enlisted the help of his younger brother, Hagen, to kill Sigurd. While Sigurd slept, Hagen slipped into his room and stabbed him. By pure chance, the knife pierced the vulnerable spot on Sigurd's back, and Sigurd drew his last breath. Brynhild's vengeance against Gudrun for stealing her lover was complete, but now Sigurd was dead. To honor her ill-fated love for Sigurd, Brynhild threw herself on his funeral pyre and died. Gudrun was almost torn apart by grief over the loss of her husband. The curse of the ring was complete: Tragedy came to all who possessed it.

BEOWULF *Celtic*

King Hrothgar of Denmark built a remarkable hall for his noblemen. Finished in silver, gold, and rare woods, Heorot Hall was more magnificent than anything anyone had ever built. It was supposed to be a place of great merriment, where mead flowed like water and men laughed and feasted. But that was not how it turned out. For nearby, in the swamps and stagnant pools, lived an evil and loathsome monster named Grendel.

Grendel despised King Hrothgar and thrived on men's misery. Each night for twelve years he had dragged his huge and hideous body out of the fen, ambled up to Heorot Hall, burst open the door with a single swipe of his filthy hand, and slaughtered dozens of men. No weapon could kill Grendel or even wound him. To do battle with him meant certain death.

News of King Hrothgar's troubles reached a young man named Beowulf, who lived across the sea in the kingdom of the Geats. Beowulf had the strength of several men and was considered invincible; he was ready for the challenge of Grendel. He assembled fifteen brave men and sailed to Denmark.

"Greetings, brave Beowulf!" said old King Hrothgar. "I will grant you anything you desire if you should succeed in killing Grendel, but I see you have brought no weapons other than an ordinary sword. I fear this won't be sufficient against the monster."

"Fear not," Beowulf assured him. "As you have learned, weapons of any kind are useless against Grendel. I am prepared to fight him hand to hand. My weapons are my own strength and the strength of my armor."

"I admire your bravery, good Beowulf. I only hope it is not wasted in an impossible battle."

That very night, as Beowulf and his men lay sleeping, Grendel stole out of the fen and burst into Heorot Hall. Immediately the monster grabbed one of the men and ate him; then just as suddenly he turned toward Beowulf. Before Grendel knew what was happening, Beowulf seized his arm and held it in a vicelike grip. Grendel bellowed in surprise and pain, and Beowulf tightened his grasp and squeezed. The ogre shook and waved his arm. He spun Beowulf around and swung him into the benches and walls. But Beowulf never loosened his hold. The rest of the men cowered and hid and ducked out of the way of the flying furniture. Finally, mustering all his strength, Beowulf tore Grendel's arm from its socket. The tremendous ripping sound of its sinews was gruesome beyond belief. In agony, and bleeding profusely, Grendel left the hall, mortally wounded.

The next morning, Beowulf was declared a hero, and he and his men were given great honors and riches. They cleaned up Heorot Hall and mounted Grendel's arm on the wall as a trophy. That night, laughter was heard in the hall for the first time in a dozen years. But it was not to last.

Though Grendel was dead, his mother lived, and she sought to avenge the death of her son. In the darkest hours, as Beowulf, King Hrothgar, and all the warriors slept, Grendel's mother approached Heorot Hall. In a flash she burst in, killed King Hrothgar's best friend, and tore Grendel's severed arm from the wall. Then just as quickly she disappeared into the night.

Beowulf, who was sleeping in a lodge a distance away from the commotion, paid a visit to the king early the next morning.

"Tragedy has struck again," lamented King Hrothgar. "Another monster, as fierce as Grendel, committed murder last night. Will there be no end to this curse?"

"Despair not, dear king," said Beowulf. "I will rid you of this new menace as surely as I slew the first."

Beowulf organized his men, and they tracked the monster to a foul pond infested by serpents. Beowulf donned his armor, slew one of the serpents, and then dove into the water in pursuit of Grendel's mother.

Down, down he swam. Darker and darker the water became.

Then the ogress spied him and began her attack. Her talons couldn't pierce his armor, and his sword couldn't penetrate her skin. She grabbed him and drew him ever deeper into the murk.

At last they arrived at an underground cavern that was dry and filled with air. Beowulf continued to battle the ogress, but soon realized that his sword was totally useless. It was then that he spotted a huge saber mounted on the wall, apparently forged by giants. Just as the ogress was preparing to deliver a fatal blow, Beowulf grabbed the enormous weapon and slew her.

Light now filled the hall, and Beowulf saw the body of Grendel. With the giant sword he cut off the head as a trophy to take back with him. Meanwhile, the blood of the slain ogress floated up to the surface of the pond, where Beowulf's men waited in dread.

"This gore cannot be a good sign," one said. "Beowulf has been down there a long time. Perhaps this is the end of him."

"We owe it to him to wait a little while longer," said another.

Beowulf then made his way slowly toward the surface, carrying Grendel's severed head. Just as the men were losing their last glimmer of hope, he broke the surface, triumphant. His men were relieved beyond measure, and together they carried Grendel's head back to King Hrothgar. Denmark was safe, and the king bestowed fabulous riches upon Beowulf and his men, which they carried home to the land of the Geats.

THE SWORD IN THE STONE *Celtic*

After the Roman Empire fell, King Uther Pendragon of Cornwall struggled to create a strong and noble Britain. To help him, he enlisted the aid of Merlin, a wise but mysterious magician. Under Merlin's direction, Uther Pendragon built a grand castle called Camelot. In it he placed a round table to accommodate a corps of knights, who would guide Britain toward glory.

In those days, a knight's honor was of the utmost importance. And it so happened that King Uther Pendragon insulted the honor of one of his knights, Gorlois, by making advances to his wife, Igerne. The offended knight had no choice but to challenge the king to a fight to the death.

The night before the battle, however, Uther Pendragon persuaded Merlin to transform him into the image of Gorlois. Reluctantly, Merlin did so. In this disguise the king spent the night with Igerne, whom Gorlois had imprisoned in a tower to protect her from the king. The next morning, Uther Pendragon, as himself again, killed Gorlois in battle. He then wed Igerne, who was pregnant with a child that both believed had been fathered by Gorlois.

Forbidden by law to raise any child other than the king's, Igerne gave over her newborn to Merlin, who entrusted the child's upbringing to Sir Hector, a knight. Sir Hector named the child Arthur and raised him along with his son, Sir Kay. Merlin never revealed Arthur's origins, and Sir Hector never asked.

A few years later, Uther died and Britain was left without a king. The knights of the Round Table had no idea whom to choose as a successor to Uther Pendragon. On Christmas Eve they assembled at a church in London and asked Merlin how this great question would be resolved.

"Uther Pendragon has left no heir, and his work is coming

undone by the squabbling of pretenders to the throne," said one of the knights.

"How can a new king be chosen who won't incite a war among his rivals?" asked another.

Merlin stroked his long, ribbonlike beard. "What you need, my lords, is a test. Something objective. Something incontestable. Some true means by which only a man worthy of being king of Britain can be selected."

"But what test do you have in mind, great wizard?" asked the knights, anxiously.

"Follow me, my lords, and all will be clear." Merlin directed the knights to the courtyard, where lay a large boulder. Atop the boulder was a black iron anvil. Thrust deep into both the anvil and the stone was a sword with a beautiful hilt.

"Behold your test," declared Merlin. As he waved his staff before the boulder the following words appeared in the rock:

> *Whosoever removes the sword from the stone*
> *Can claim this kingdom as his own.*

Each knight tried his hand at removing the sword from the stone, but none could budge it. People came from all across the land to try to pull the sword free, but years went by and no one succeeded.

One day, a jousting tournament in London was announced. Knights came from all over, including Sir Kay. This was to be his first tournament, and he was very excited. Arthur, now near the age of fifteen, accompanied him. While Sir Kay was practicing for the tournament, he accidentally broke his sword and sent Arthur back home to fetch a new one.

"Time is wasting, brother," he said. "Ride like the wind and bring me back a new sword."

But when Arthur got home, the metalsmith's shop was closed, and no sword could be found. He rode back toward London, greatly upset because he could not aid his brother. As he rode past a churchyard, a gleam of light hit his eye. He turned and noticed the shining hilt of a sword protruding from an anvil on a rock. As he drew closer, he thought, "No one will notice if I borrow this sword. I will return it as soon as Sir Kay is finished competing in the tournament."

With no effort at all, the boy took hold of the sword's hilt and pulled it from the stone. Then off he went to deliver it to Sir Kay.

"Where on earth did you get this?" said the astonished Kay, who recognized the weapon immediately as the sword in the stone.

"I am sorry, brother," apologized Arthur, "there was no sword to be had at home, so I had to bring you this one. I found it in a churchyard."

"Well done!" said Sir Kay. "But you may get into trouble for removing it from the church grounds. Let us just say that it was I who took it."

"Yes, brother," agreed Arthur gratefully.

Sir Kay called over his father, Sir Hector, and announced that he had removed the sword in the stone. Sir Hector didn't believe him, so the three men rode back to the churchyard and Sir Kay placed the sword back into the stone. But once the sword was reinserted, he couldn't remove it again.

"Here, let me show you," said Arthur, as he grasped the sword's hilt and lifted it effortlessly.

A crowd began to gather. Repeatedly the sword was replaced in its original position, and repeatedly, only Arthur could remove it. It was clear to all: Arthur was destined to be king of Britain.

GILGAMESH AND ENKIDU *Babylonian*

Gilgamesh was one-third god and stronger, braver, and more handsome than any man. As king of the magnificent city of Uruk, he was also a bit of a tyrant. "I have no equal," declared Gilgamesh proudly, though in his heart he secretly wished for a friend just like himself.

After years of suffering under Gilgamesh's rule, paying high taxes and laboring hard to build his stone city, the people of Uruk prayed to the gods for mercy. Their cry went out: "Please, goddess Aruru, put Gilgamesh in his place, for he is out of control and cruel beyond measure."

Aruru heard their pleas and from clay crafted Enkidu, a man as strong and courageous as Gilgamesh, but covered like an animal with shaggy hair. At first Enkidu lived like an animal, too, running and foraging among the deer, drinking with the cattle, grazing with the gazelles.

One night Gilgamesh had a troubling dream. He was engaged in fierce battle with someone as strong as himself. He had never had such a dream before, so he mentioned it to his mother, who had the gift of prophesy.

"Don't you worry about that dream, my son," his mother told him. "This mysterious new adversary is destined to become your friend." Reassured, Gilgamesh gave the dream no further thought.

Though Enkidu was as innocent as an animal, he was also smarter. As he roamed with the animals, he filled in the pit traps set by hunters and tore down their nets so that his animal friends could go unharmed. One day a hunter out inspecting his traps saw Enkidu at a watering hole. Alarmed and frightened by Enkidu's shaggy, half-human appearance, the hunter concealed himself, and witnessed Enkidu spoiling his traps and drinking among the animals. Each day the hunter reset the traps, and each day he would

49

watch the man-beast destroying them. Distressed by the loss of his livelihood, the hunter appealed to Gilgamesh for help.

"This man that you describe as so shaggy and so uncivilized needs to be shown the ways of men," said Gilgamesh to the hunter. "Do not be afraid of him, for if he is as you describe, he is all innocence. Take a temple mistress with you and camp by the watering hole. This man-beast will see her and be smitten. Then he will lose his innocence and trouble you no further."

The hunter did as he was bidden, and the plan worked. Enkidu was intrigued by the mistress and passed a week with her. When he went to rejoin the animals, they ran from him as if he were a stranger.

"They no longer recognize you," the mistress, a prostitute, told Enkidu. "Before you were like an animal, but now you are like a man. Come with me to Uruk, and there I will introduce you to Gilgamesh, the king."

The prostitute presented Enkidu to Gilgamesh. "Here is the man whose strength might rival yours, great king," she said.

"Impossible!" snapped Gilgamesh.

"Well, there is only one way to find out," she said, to goad him.

Gilgamesh and Enkidu began to battle with all their might. First one got the upper hand, and then the other. To the very end the outcome was undetermined. Then Gilgamesh pinned Enkidu to the floor. And at that very moment, he remembered his dream.

"Friend!" he shouted triumphantly, helping Enkidu to stand.

"Friend!" Enkidu replied. The two embraced, sealing their friendship. When Gilgamesh's mother met Enkidu, she adopted him into the family.

The two men were as close as brothers could be, but one day Enkidu felt saddened over the loss of his animal-like strength. To restore Enkidu's confidence, Gilgamesh suggested an adventure.

"We have not yet made names for ourselves, brother. Let us go to the Mountain of Cedars and cut down one of the sacred trees."

"But Gilgamesh," protested Enkidu, "the journey is very far and no one has ever returned. The Mountain of Cedars is the sacred forest of the gods. Once a man enters he is unlikely to come out, for it is guarded by Humbaba, who is as fierce as a lion, fast as lightning, unstoppable as a raging river, and can hear a cow grazing in a pasture twenty miles away. Think of what you are saying."

"I know what I'm saying," replied Gilgamesh. "I say we go to the forest and kill Humbaba. If we succeed, our names will live forever as those who accomplished this task. If we fail, we will forever be known as the two who were brave enough to try."

"I beg you not to attempt this foolishness," protested Enkidu.

"I will not be dissuaded," said Gilgamesh. "Even now I am preparing a sacrifice to Shamash, our protector god."

That night, Gilgamesh dreamed he was standing at the foot of a tall mountain. Fire blazed in the sky, the earth shook and rumbled, trees crashed to the ground, and thunder deafened him. As he stood, the mountain suddenly toppled and flattened at his feet. The next morning, Gilgamesh told Enkidu about this dream.

"This is a sign of victory, Gilgamesh," said Enkidu. "Shamash is with us. I will go with you and assist you in this brave but reckless pursuit."

Their long, arduous journey ended at the sacred cedar forest. Gilgamesh immediately began to cut down one of the trees. From miles away, Humbaba heard the sound and rushed to its source.

"Who dares to touch my trees?" roared Humbaba, his voice like those of twenty demons.

Seeing Humbaba's ferocity, Gilgamesh lost courage. But then Shamash appeared as a wild and fast-blowing wind. It surrounded Humbaba, stinging his eyes and pinning him to the spot.

Gilgamesh resumed his chopping. "It is I, Gilgamesh, king of Uruk," he said as he chopped. As Humbaba crouched helplessly, Gilgamesh and Enkidu felled seven cedars. Then they approached the frightened Humbaba.

"Have mercy on me," cried Humbaba. "If you let me live, I will be your servant. You may have the trees for your own use."

"Don't trust him, Gilgamesh," shouted Enkidu. "Remember we have come to defeat Humbaba. He will turn on you. Kill him now!"

Gilgamesh drew his sword and struck Humbaba in the neck. Enkidu struck him a second time. Then Gilgamesh drew the last and final blow. Humbaba fell to the ground, and the entire cedar forest, now without a guardian, began trembling.

Ishtar, the goddess of love and war, witnessed the spectacle and was impressed by Gilgamesh's masculine beauty and courage. She appeared before him. "Gilgamesh, come and be my lover. I will be your wife. We will sit like king and queen before all other royalty."

"Ishtar, lovely goddess," replied Gilgamesh, "how many times have you uttered those words to other men? And what awaits me if I become your husband? A miserable and cursed existence, like that of all your previous husbands? I'd like to say I'm flattered by your offer, but it rings hollow in my ears."

"How dare you!" screamed the goddess. "I have never been so insulted! You'll pay dearly for your insolence, Gilgamesh. Just you wait." Saying this, Ishtar went to her father and told him what had happened. "Father, my honor is at stake here! I order you to create a giant celestial bull and set it loose to devour Gilgamesh and his shaggy friend."

Gilgamesh and Enkidu were trekking back home when they heard a rumbling behind them. They turned to see a snorting bull of enormous proportions charging at them. Gilgamesh fought the bull but needed Enkidu's help to subdue it. Ishtar appeared nearby, shouting insults. Enkidu killed the bull and tore it into pieces. Ishtar stood speechless, and Enkidu threw one of the bull's bloody limbs at her. "Here is what we'll do to you if you continue to hound us!" he said. Fuming, the goddess disappeared to plot her revenge. Meanwhile, Gilgamesh and Enkidu returned home, heroes who defeated Humbaba and lived to tell about it.

The Hare and the Hyena

Various Tribes/African

Times were hard and food was scarce. Hare and Hyena both took jobs weeding a farmer's field. Their payment was to be a pot of beans each day. In the morning the two animals set up a fire so the beans could simmer while they labored. Soon the sun was high in the sky, and Hare and Hyena stopped for their midday break. By now the beans were cooked and ready to eat.

"I'm going down to the stream to wash up before lunch," said Hyena. "You stay here and stir the pot. I'll be right back."

The instant that Hyena was beyond Hare's view, he peeled off his skin. Hyenas, which aren't terribly attractive with their skins on, are surpassingly ugly without them. Skinless, Hyena ran back to Hare, flailing his arms and uttering all sorts of wailing, monstrous sounds. Thinking that Hyena was some sort of vile beast, Hare was absolutely terrified. He dropped the ladle and ran out of sight as quickly as his haunches could carry him.

With Hare gone, Hyena picked up the ladle, sat down, and enjoyed a leisurely lunch, eating both his and Hare's portions. Emitting a hearty burp, he got up, retrieved his skin, and went back to the pot.

By this time, Hare figured the coast was clear and ventured back to the pot.

"Where's my lunch?" Hyena demanded, acting all perplexed.

"Didn't you see?" asked Hare. "A ferocious monster came just as you left to wash up. He frightened me away, and I guess he ate all the beans."

"Not likely," snapped Hyena. "I think you ate the beans."

"I swear I didn't. It happened just as I described it, whether you believe me or not. Anyway, if I see that monster again, I'm going to be ready for it. Look, I'm making a bow and some arrows.

If it comes back, I'll shoot it."

"Let me see that bow," said Hyena. "You're not doing it right. Let me help." He took the bow and, pretending to carve it into shape, weakened the wood. "Here, now you have a bow worthy of killing a monster."

The two went back to work. Poor Hare, weak from hunger, couldn't fail to notice that Hyena seemed unusually content and awfully energetic.

The next day, when the noontime break came around, Hyena once again excused himself to wash up. Hare tended the beans and kept his bow and arrows close at hand. Sure enough, Hyena had been gone only a minute when the monster once again arrived to menace poor Hare. But Hare was ready: He grabbed an arrow, placed it in the bow and—*snap!* The bow split in two. The monster came closer. Hare threw down his useless weapon, turned tail and fled.

When Hare returned, Hyena once again scolded him for eating all the beans. But by now Hare was on to him. That evening, Hare made a new bow, which he kept hidden from Hyena. When lunchtime rolled around the next day and the monster once again appeared, Hare shot him in the leg. The monster fled, allowing Hare to savor the entire pot of beans himself. A little later, when Hyena came limping back, he had a lot of explaining to do!

THE OGRE *Swahili/African*

One day, a little girl was playing by the sea with her friends when she happened upon a beautiful seashell.

"How lovely it is!" she exclaimed. "I'll just put it on this big boulder so I won't lose it, then I'll take it home to be my new lucky charm." The children spent the day at the beach, and, when the light began to fade, they headed home. The little girl forgot about the shell until she was almost at her village.

"My shell!" she exclaimed. "I have to go back and get it! Who wants to come with me?"

"Not me," said one friend. "I'm tired."

"It's dinnertime, and I'm starved," said another.

"It's almost dark out," said the third.

"It's just a simple shell," said the fourth. "It'll be there tomorrow."

But the little girl would not be put off. The shell was her lucky charm, and she wanted it that instant, so she headed off alone under the rosy sky. The dark shadows were long and the walk was creepy, so she made up a little song to keep herself company:

> *My shell, my shell, my beautiful shell,*
> *My shell, my shell, it treats me well.*
> *My shell, my shell, with colors bright,*
> *My shell, my shell, means luck tonight.*

When she got to the boulder where she had left the shell, an ogre was sitting on it. He was big and broad and more than seven feet tall, with coarse hair all over his body. His head was bald and he had two mouths, each lined with jagged, broken teeth. He wore a ragged loincloth made of leopard skin. His large, filthy feet bore six toes each, and his fingernails and toenails were long and curved. He sat on the boulder, idly tossing the shell up in the air and catching it in his beefy hands.

"Hello, little girl," he said sweetly. "What a lovely voice you have. Is this the shell you're looking for?" He continued tossing the shell from one hand to the other.

"Um . . . I'm not sure," she replied hesitantly. Though she was frightened by the ogre, his apparently gentle disposition calmed her. "The light's too dim, and I can't see it."

"Come closer, child." The ogre beckoned. "Lucky shells don't come around too often."

When the little girl drew closer, the ogre grabbed her and stuffed her into a big drum he had hidden behind the boulder. "Sweet child," he said as he stretched the skin over the top of the drum, "your voice is like honey, and it will earn a fortune for me."

The ogre took the drum from one village to the next, putting on a show everywhere he went.

"I have a magic drum," he declared to the residents. "As I beat it, it sings in time to the rhythm. For a donation of food or gold, I shall show you." He then would strike a rhythm on the drum, and the little girl inside would sing. People were amazed wherever he performed, and soon he had all the chickens and vegetables and cakes and beer he wanted. But he fed the little girl just enough to keep her alive.

In his travels, the ogre stopped in the little girl's own village to perform. Her singing caught the attention of the girl's grieving parents, who recognized her voice. Happy that she was alive but horrified at what had become of her, they quickly thought up a plan.

"Your drum is truly magical," the father said to the ogre at the end of his performance. "Please come back and play for us tomorrow. I promise to reward you for your troubles."

The ogre promised to come back, and he retreated into the woods for the night. The girl's parents quickly told the villagers of their suspicions. They collected as much beer as they could and waited until morning.

The next day, the ogre reappeared with his drum. Knowing that ogres have a weakness for beer, the father told him that the village was famous for its brews, and invited the ogre to sample all the different kinds in payment for his playing. The ogre drank and played, played and drank. Soon, he just drank. Then he fell into a deep, drunken sleep.

The father quickly opened the drum and freed his daughter. While her mother took her into the house for a bath and some food, her father filled the drum with poisonous snakes, bees, and fire ants. Then he carefully resealed the drum. After a while, he awakened the ogre.

"Please play some more, sir," begged the father. "We have some guests in town who have not yet heard your drum."

The ogre picked up his stick and struck the drum, but no singing came from it.

"Perhaps the magic is out of it," suggested a villager.

"We're out of beer anyway," said the father.

"No beer, no music!" bellowed the ogre, and he stormed out of the village with his drum.

When he was deep in the woods, he struck the drum again, but again it refused to sing.

"I'll see what's making you so silent!" he shouted at the drum as he unlaced it. Immediately he was set upon by the bees and snakes and ants, and he died a horrible death.

EDSHU CAUSES CONFLICT *Yoruban/African*

Always looking to cause mischief, Edshu, the trickster god, happened upon a path that divided two fields. The fields were owned by two neighbors who were also the best of friends. It was a bright, sunny morning, and they were out tilling the soil when Edshu spotted them. He saw his opportunity, and he took it.

Donning a hat that was red on one side and white on the other, Edshu strolled the path between the two fields, mumbling to himself, skipping, and ignoring the farmers completely. The farmers, not used to seeing strangers on the path, were fascinated by this curious and not-too-friendly fellow. They watched him as he crossed the fields, mounted a hill, then passed out of sight.

The farmers, still standing in their fields, turned to each other, shrugged their shoulders, and went back to work. A while later, they had to walk to town for supplies, and they took this opportunity to talk about the stranger they had seen that morning.

"Did you see that odd fellow with the white hat? What do you make of him?" asked the first farmer.

"He was odd, all right. But his hat was red, not white," said the second farmer.

"No, it was white," retorted the first.

"Sorry, red," insisted the second.

"Clearly, it was white."

"Not a chance. It was red."

They kept this up all the way into town, and when they could not convince each other with words, they started using their fists. Soon they were rolling around in the street, insulting each other between punches.

The townsfolk, shocked at such behavior, managed to separate the fighting farmers. They brought them before the head of the village, who heard their arguments as the townsfolk looked on.

"We both saw the stranger. But I say his hat was white!" shouted the first farmer.

"Even an idiot could see that the hat was red!" snapped the second farmer.

By now the townspeople had started taking sides as to which farmer was correct. The crowd began to get loud and unruly.

"Gentlemen," said the village leader, quieting the crowd, "I don't know how to resolve this. You are both equally convinced about what you saw. You both seem sober and sane. There's no explaining how one can see red and one can see white."

Unsatisfied, the crowd buzzed and roared. Almost everyone, it seemed, had an opinion on this issue. Then, just as a riot was about to break out, Edshu pushed his way to the front of the crowd. Waving the offending hat in the air, he explained his joke.

"Here is the hat that caused all this trouble. Trouble is exactly what I had in mind. The farmers couldn't help but fight. I wanted it that way—spreading strife is my greatest joy."

How Tricksters Get Tricked
Algonquin/Native American

When Glooskap, the creator god and trickster, was in his mother's womb with his twin brother, Malsum, they discussed how they would be born. "I will enter the world as carefully as possible," said Glooskap.

"Not me," said Malsum. "I will find another way."

When the time of their birth came, Glooskap was born naturally. Malsum, however, tore his way out through his mother's abdomen, killing her.

Glooskap was the good brother. He was handsome, smart, and well liked. He created the world from his mother's body and also formed the sun, moon, most of the animals, and humans. Malsum was the evil brother—creator of serpents, insurmountable mountains, desolate valleys, and all other challenging features of earth.

The brothers were immortal, but each of them could be killed by an ordinary object—they both kept theirs a closely guarded secret. As the two chatted one day, they shared a rare moment of brotherly warmth. Taking advantage of the moment, Malsum slyly asked Glooskap if he ever thought about death.

"I don't think about it too often, because I am practically immune to it," replied Glooskap.

"What do you mean 'practically immune'?" asked Malsum.

"I mean that only the prick of an owl feather can kill me."

"Hmm, how interesting," responded Malsum, filing this morsel of information for later use. "I guess I am practically immune to death, also. I am invulnerable to everything except being hit by a fern root." Malsum then bade his brother farewell and went off, to do some mischief, no doubt.

Time passed and Glooskap all but forgot the forboding conversation he had with his brother. But Malsum had not. While

Glooskap slept, Malsum, who was always jealous of his more attractive, smarter, and better-liked brother, caught an owl and plucked one of its feathers. He sneaked into Glooskap's bedchamber and poked him with the feather's sharp end. Glooskap died.

Malsum's elation over his brother's death was short-lived. Glooskap had powerful magic that Malsum underestimated. He used this magic to bring himself back to life. Suspecting that his brother was responsible for his death, he set about to trap him. While washing himself in a river, Glooskap pretended to be muttering to himself, but made a point of speaking loudly enough to be heard by anyone who might be spying on him. "That was a close brush with death," he said. "Luckily, the only thing that can kill me forever is the flowering reed."

A beaver overheard Glooskap and figured he could use this information for personal gain. He wasted no time finding Malsum.

"I know what will truly kill Glooskap," the beaver announced to Malsum.

"If you will tell me, I'll give you anything you want—after Glooskap is dead."

"Agreed!" said the beaver. "Glooskap can be killed with a flowering reed. Now after you kill him, you have to promise to make me fly."

"Fly! You?" laughed Malsum. "With a body and tail like that? You'd look ridiculous. Be serious."

The beaver, who was serious, was now deeply offended and regretted telling Malsum anything. He raced to warn Glooskap that his brother knew his secret.

Glooskap thanked the beaver and then went off to the woods to dig the roots of a fern. He returned home and hid them under his pillow. Later that night, Glooskap pretended to be asleep. In the wee hours of the morning, before the sun rose, his door opened and in walked Malsum, clutching a fistful of flowering reeds. He crept quietly over to Glooskap's side and, believing his brother to be asleep, poked him with the reeds. Glooskap made a loud gasp and pretended to be dead. Malsum, thrilled to have vanquished his brother at long last, laughed and danced merrily over Glooskap's inert body. Suddenly Glooskap bolted upright. Malsum gave a yelp of surprise and jumped high off the ground.

"Evil brother," boomed Glooskap, "you have tried to kill me twice. I'm getting tired of your foul antics." From beneath his pillow he drew the fern roots. Malsum was frozen with terror. "I hoped I wouldn't have to resort to this, but it is clear that the world cannot tolerate both of us. Good-bye, brother." He lobbed the roots at Malsum. They pierced his heart and he fell down, dead.

With Malsum out of the way, Glooskap was free to tend to the matters of the world. He defeated the ogres and giant serpents, the goblins and cannibals, the sorcerers and evil spirits, and other nasty creatures that Malsum had put on the earth for his own amusement. All these victories made Glooskap very proud, and he declared himself invincible.

"You call yourself invincible," said a wise woman one day, "but there is someone who has not been conquered, and he may be your match."

"Impossible," said Glooskap. "Who is this challenger and what are his powers?"

"His name is Wasis," replied the woman. "You should meet him yourself."

"Then bring me to him."

The woman took Glooskap to her humble home, where, on the floor, sucking a piece of maple candy, was an infant. "This is Wasis," declared the woman proudly.

"A baby?" blurted a surprised Glooskap. "This little baby is my match? This must be a joke."

"True, he's a baby," said the woman. "But Wasis has a will that no magic can break."

"We shall see," said Glooskap.

Glooskap was a little nervous, since he had never really been around babies before, but he figured that Wasis should be easy to master. Wasis sat there, sucking his candy, making little cooing noises. "Come here, little Wasis," said Glooskap softly. The baby looked at him and smiled, but didn't move. Glooskap made beautiful bird noises, which briefly caught the baby's attention, but then he became bored and ignored the hero.

Angered at such disrespectful treatment, Glooskap shouted at Wasis, "Come here, child!" But the baby just started wailing. Glooskap tried curses and spells, but they just further irritated the baby, who screamed louder and louder. Glooskap raised his voice over the din of the baby, but that, too, made the baby increase his own pitch. Glooskap couldn't outshout the baby, so he resorted to songs. Wasis quieted down, but once again assumed the same bored expression. Still he wouldn't come to Glooskap.

Exasperated, Glooskap ran from the house, admitting defeat. "Goo-goo," said the baby to his mother. And ever after, babies have said "goo-goo" to commemorate the day that the baby Wasis outsmarted Glooskap the trickster.

3

LOVE AND LOVERS

WHO DOESN'T ENJOY A LOVE STORY? Every culture has its share
of legendary couples fated to be separated by circumstances yet
reunited in the end. In these memorable tales, cruelly parted lovers
must exhibit superhuman courage and endure agonizing tests of
faith, and often of intelligence, before they are reunited.

The obstacles the lovers face are often put before them by the
gods or by rivals, either out of jealousy or because of some merely
imagined slight. Sometimes the lovers are used as pawns between
competing deities. Though gods and goddesses may work various
forms of magic in these stories, the real appeal comes from the
lovers themselves. With unwavering determination, these mortals
overcome extraordinary challenges and powerful forces in order to
be together. Some even defy death.

These love stories are as moving as any written today—and the
endings are almost always happy. But in addition to their entertaining plots, these tales carry a message. They are stories of
faith—not only in the ultimate goodness of the gods but also in
oneself and one's convictions. Empowered by love, a person can
accomplish what at first seems impossible.

The heroines and heroes in these tales uphold the highest
moral standards, respecting both the gods and their fellow mortals.
Even though separation from their loved ones is agonizing and
harsh, they never become vindictive or deceitful. Ultimately, these
stories demonstrate that iron faith and shining morality in the service of love are the strongest forces of all, capable of softening the
heart of the most irate god and allowing the individual to accomplish remarkable tasks. No matter how bleak the circumstances
may seem, in the end, love will prevail.

CUPID AND PSYCHE *Roman*

Once there lived a young woman named Psyche, whose beauty was so legendary that people came from miles away just to see her. Young men fought for her hand, and artisans clamored to paint her picture or carve her image in stone.

Frustrated that her suitors could not see beyond her beauty, one day Psyche complained to her father. "You have taken great pains to educate me, but nobody cares that I have opinions about the world and can speak five languages. When people look at me, all they see is my beauty. Such beauty will be my downfall, I am sure."

"Patience, child," her father replied. "Someday happiness will come your way. There are worse things than being beautiful."

So Psyche endured the attention that the people heaped upon her. "She's more beautiful than Venus herself!" they declared.

Psyche wasn't the only one who disliked the attention she was receiving. Venus, the goddess of love, found comparisons between herself and a mortal to be intolerable. To her, beauty was the highest ideal, and she was being compared with a mortal! Venus was infuriated and decided to put an end to it.

"Cupid," she called to her son, the god of love and romantic desire, "please help your mother with a little errand. A mortal girl named Psyche rivals me in beauty. Put her in her place. Make her fall in love with someone ugly and repulsive."

"Yes, Mother," replied the winged god. He flew down to earth and visited Psyche as she slept. Even Cupid was moved by her beauty. Going about his errand, he touched her with one of his arrows of desire, and she opened her eyes. This so startled Cupid that he accidentally pricked himself with the arrow. Suddenly he fell deeply in love with her. Their destiny had been sealed. But Cupid vowed to keep his love for Psyche a secret, for fear of his mother's wrath.

Time went by, and though suitors still came to pay tribute to Psyche's beauty, no one asked for her hand in marriage. "It's strange," thought her father. "Suitors used to come in droves. Psyche's two sisters, who were half as bright and perhaps even a little selfish, had no trouble finding husbands. Could Psyche have been cursed?"

Psyche's parents went to the oracle of Apollo to seek a solution. "Your daughter is destined to marry a monster whom neither mortals nor gods can resist," said the oracle. "He awaits her at the top of the mountain. You must bring her there and leave her."

Psyche's parents were filled with grief and horror, but they could not disobey the oracle. They brought Psyche to the craggy mountaintop. "As I predicted, my beauty has become my downfall. I must accept my fate," said Psyche stoically. She kissed her parents for what was likely to be the last time.

Left on the summit, Psyche shivered with fear as she awaited her mate. Soon a gentle breeze lifted her into the air and carried her to a flowery field, where it let her down. "Well, that wasn't unpleasant," thought Psyche. In fact, the experience relaxed her, so she lay down in the field and took a nap. She awoke beside a grand mansion on beautiful grounds. Astonished at its magnificence, she was drawn inside. The interior was equally impressive, filled with art and beautiful furnishings.

"Everything you see is yours," said a voice, but Psyche saw no one in the room. "We are your servants," said another voice from an invisible source. "Have a seat and enjoy your dinner." Psyche sat at the banquet table, and ample food and drink were carried out to her by invisible hands. Invisible musicians performed as she dined, and when she was finished, the dishes were just as mysteriously taken away.

Only later, when the night was at its darkest, did Psyche meet her husband. He was kind and gentle to her, and he awoke passion in her. But he was gone by the first glimmer of morning, promising to return that night. After several passionate nights, Psyche begged to see her husband's face.

"Please do not ask to see me," said her husband. "We are in love, and that is all that matters."

Psyche accepted those terms, but soon her thoughts turned to her parents and sisters. "They don't know my happy fate, and I wish to see them again," she told her husband.

"As you wish," he said reluctantly, and the next morning, a gentle wind carried Psyche to the valley of her sisters. Her sisters were thrilled to see her. "Come to my house," Psyche invited them, "and see how I live."

The wind carried Psyche and her two sisters back to the mansion, where their every whim was catered to by invisible servants. "Very impressive," said the oldest sister, more than a little jealous of her sister's good fortune.

"What's your husband like?" asked the second sister. Psyche described how wonderfully kind and passionate her husband was, but then admitted that she'd never actually seen him.

"Remember, dear sister," said the older sister, "the oracle said you were to marry a monster. Perhaps your husband is just making you fat and happy so he can devour you."

"Take a lamp and a knife with you to bed," said the second sister. "As your husband sleeps, light the lamp and see what he looks like. If he is a monster—which he probably is—kill him with the knife."

"Don't be silly. My husband is no monster," said Psyche, laughing uncomfortably. But the idea had lodged itself in her head, and she really couldn't resist the plan. One night as her husband slept she lit a lamp and leaned over him. But instead of a horrible monster, Psyche gazed at the beautiful face of Cupid. Incredulous, she leaned a little closer. Some burning oil spilled from the lamp onto the god's shoulder, awakening him. He looked up at Psyche, then darted out of bed.

"Is this how you repay your love, by breaking your promise? If you prefer your sisters' words to mine, then go back to them. Love cannot dwell with suspicion, dear Psyche. I can stay with you no longer." Unfolding his snowy wings, he flew out the window, deaf to Psyche's cries and protests. The mansion and its grounds fell to ruins, leaving Psyche with nothing.

Psyche roamed the land, searching futilely for her husband. Eventually she arrived at a magnificent temple. Hoping that she might find him there, she entered. Instead she found garden tools, ears of corn, and sacks of grain strewn about. "This temple belongs to Ceres, the goddess of the harvest," thought Psyche. In her piety, Psyche spent the day cleaning and organizing the disheveled temple. When she was done, Ceres herself appeared to her.

"I am touched by your devotion, Psyche," said the goddess. "But it is Venus whose favor you must win before you can get Cupid back. I suggest you appeal to her directly. If you make yourself her servant, perhaps you will win her forgiveness."

Psyche thanked Ceres and went off to find the temple of Venus, though she was skeptical about the results. At the temple, Venus appeared to Psyche. "So, at last you pay your respects to me," scolded the goddess. "Or are you just concerned about your husband? He's recuperating from the burn that you inflicted on his shoulder. The effects of that wound are not half as bad as the damage he did to himself with his own arrow. Imagine . . . falling in love with a mortal!" Before Psyche could respond, Venus continued, "If you want to be my son's wife, you must prove yourself worthy. In the back of this temple is a storeroom where assorted seeds are kept for my pigeons. You must separate the seeds into piles—each pile with a single variety of seed. And have it done by nightfall!" Then, Venus vanished.

Psyche opened the storeroom door. The floor was piled two feet high with all manner of seeds. She began the task, but after a few minutes realized it was futile. "This is impossible," she cried. "I will never win Venus' favor and I will never see Cupid again!" As she sat sobbing, Cupid, who was watching from Mount Olympus, felt pity and sent in an army of busy ants. Grain by grain they separated the seeds until all were sorted neatly into piles.

At twilight Venus returned and, to her consternation, found the job completed. "This is just the beginning, wretched child!" the goddess of love shrieked. "I will have other chores for you to per-form!" And in a flash she was gone.

The next morning Venus reappeared to Psyche to present the next task. She took her to a field and said, "Past those trees is a rag-ing river, and past the river grazes a flock of sheep with fleece of gold. Bring me some golden fleece from each of those sheep."

Psyche went to the riverside, but the water raged and the cur-rent was strong. "Even if I could cross this dangerous river, the sheep on the other side look fierce and wild," she thought. "They would never allow me to pluck their wool." As Psyche sat on the bank thinking of a plan, the river god rose up in front of her.

"Dear Psyche," he said, "I can slow these treacherous currents so you may cross in safety, but you must wait until noon, when the rams will grow weary in the heat and will retire to the shade. Then you can collect bits of their golden wool caught on the bushes and tree trunks."

Psyche easily accomplished her mission and returned to Venus carrying an armload of shimmering wool.

"If the other gods weren't on your side," said Venus angrily, "you would be incapable of doing anything. I'm thoroughly worn out by this whole sad affair, and now I fear I've lost some of my beauty through worrying about you and my son. So I have another task for you." Venus handed a small, ornate box to Psyche. "Take this box and go to the underworld. Tell Proserpine, the queen of the under-world, to fill it with an offering for me. And be quick about it!"

Psyche took the box with trembling fingers. She had no choice but to obey the irate goddess. She was sure now that her life was finished. She reasoned that the fastest way to the underworld was to die, and she was about to throw herself off a cliff, when she heard a voice. "Beautiful Psyche," said the voice, "do you think that the gods would assist you this far only to abandon you? Listen well, and I will tell you how to reach the underworld and also how to return to the land of the living."

"Why, thank you. I will be ever in your debt," said Psyche, breathing a sigh of relief. "But who are you?"

"Never mind who I am. Just think of me as your friend." The voice then told Psyche all the hazards she would encounter on her journey to the underworld and how best to overcome them. "Listen well, child," the voice concluded. "Do not open the box once Proserpine fills it with beauty. This is meant for goddesses only and is of no use to a mortal woman."

Psyche thanked her adviser and then departed for the land of the dead. The journey was difficult, but she endured. She was consoled by her advance notice of what was to come. Eventually she approached Proserpine's throne and was amazed by the goddess's bright radiance in a world so drab and depressing. Psyche shyly announced her mission, and Proserpine sent a servant to fill the box. Grateful that things were going so well, Psyche thanked the goddess and began her trip back.

Once she reached daylight, Psyche began to muse about the box's contents. "What could possibly be in the box? Immortality? I could live with Cupid forever! Great knowledge? I could outsmart Venus and find my true love." She could resist the temptation no longer. She opened the box. Instead, it was filled with a sleeping potion. Psyche was overcome with slumber and fell into a death-like sleep.

Cupid had by now let his immense love for Psyche conquer his anger and could no longer resist being away from her. He left Olympus and found his beloved lying in the road. "Once again, my love, your curiosity has gotten you into trouble. Even so, I do love you." He drew the slumber from her and put it back into the box, then gently awakened Psyche.

"Cupid!" exclaimed Psyche the moment she regained her senses.

"Yes, my love. I will never leave you again. But first, wait here. There is an errand I must complete." Cupid returned to Olympus. He pleaded with Venus to let him keep Psyche as his wife.

"Mother, you have repeatedly tested Psyche's love for me, and still she persists," said Cupid. "You have also tried everything in your power to cure me of my arrow wound. Don't you see, the wound is healed, and I still love Psyche."

"But she's a mortal!" cried Venus.

"Love knows no bounds," replied Cupid. "You know this. You are love's goddess. Why deny your own son's success in love?"

"Your strength as a god has grown to rival my own," Venus admitted. "Your love is too powerful for even me to control. You must follow your heart." She gave her son her blessing.

Cupid then flew to Jupiter and begged him to grant Psyche immortality and to allow her to live among the gods. Jupiter, having a weakness for romance, consented.

The ecstatic Cupid returned to Psyche, carrying a cup of ambrosia, the gods' elixir of immortality. "Here, my love, drink this, and be a goddess and be my wife."

Psyche drank from the cup and was filled with a profound sense of warmth and well-being. She and Cupid lived happily and eternally among the gods.

TRISTRAM AND ISEULT *Celtic*

King Mark of Cornwall, in southwest Britain, had a problem. His knights were notoriously inept or cowardly, and now an Irish prince named Moraunt had arrived at his gates demanding a hefty tribute. Moraunt was no ordinary knight; he was a man of enormous proportions, and he carried a poisoned lance, no less. King Mark's knights flatly refused to fight him, but Mark's young nephew, Tristram, volunteered for the task.

"But you're not even a knight—you can't challenge Moraunt," protested King Mark.

"Then knight me, Uncle. I don't see that there's much of a choice. Moraunt is bleeding our treasury. Somebody has to act, and you know I'm good with the lance."

"You're right about that," said the king.

A ceremony was prepared and young Tristram hastily became Sir Tristram, a knight in King Mark's court.

On the day of the fight, Moraunt looked formidable riding his tall steed and wearing his heavy armor. The spectators held their breath as young Tristram rode in, looking gallant and brave, but certainly less battle-worn. The two adversaries clashed and darted, testing each other. Finally, Moraunt thrust his lance, gashing Tristram's arm with its poisoned point. But Tristram held his own and, mustering all his strength, he drove the point of his lance into Moraunt's skull, mortally wounding him. The impact shattered Tristram's lance, leaving a piece of it buried in his adversary's head.

Moraunt sailed back to Ireland, where he eventually died. Meanwhile, the poison from Moraunt's lance prevented Tristram's wound from healing. With the king's permission, Tristram set sail for England to search for someone who could cure him. But a storm drove the ship off course, and he landed in a strange country.

Not knowing where he was but grateful to be alive, he began

to play his lute. The strains of his intriguing music filtered into the castle of a king who was enjoying the view from the tower with his daughter. They sent for this strange musician and welcomed him to their castle.

"What land is this?" asked Tristram.

"You are in Ireland. I am king of this land, and this is my daughter, Iseult. And who are you?"

"I am Tramtris," replied Tristram, realizing he was in the land of the enemy he had slain. "I am a minstrel and poet."

"But you are hurt!" exclaimed Iseult, noticing the wound. "I am skilled in the healing arts. Let me help you."

Iseult cured Tristram's wound, and in return Tristram taught her how to play the lute. In the process, he fell secretly in love with her. One day, a servant going through Tristram's room noticed that his lance had a broken tip. She grew suspicious.

"Madam," she said to Iseult, "forgive me for what I am about to suggest, but I have a bad feeling. Master Tramtris's lance has the end broken off. Have you kept the fatal shard you retrieved from the skull of your brother, Moraunt?"

"I have the shard, but I think your imagination is getting the better of you. Come, let us match it to the broken lance."

Iseult's fragment fit Tristram's lance perfectly. Iseult was horrified, since she had already grown quite fond of her mysterious minstrel. When the queen learned that Tristram was the one who had killed her son, she demanded his execution. Iseult pleaded for mercy, and Tristram was sent back to Cornwall and forbidden ever to set foot again in Ireland.

When Tristram arrived back in Cornwall, he told King Mark about the lovely and gracious princess Iseult and how she had saved his life not once, but twice—by healing his wound and forestalling his execution.

"She sounds like a wonderful woman," agreed the king. "I think she will make a suitable wife."

"Oh, I agree!" said Tristram.

"I want you to go back to Ireland and win the hand of the fair

Iseult in my name, then escort her safely to me so that she and I may be wed," said the king.

"Uh, Iseult—and you? Uh, yes. I-I see," stammered Tristram, realizing where his duty lay. "I am in your service, my lord." Tristram's loyalty to his king was total, and he would do anything the ruler wished, even bring to him the woman whom he himself loved. The practical problem, in Tristram's mind, was how to go back to Ireland, since a death sentence awaited him there. He decided to set sail and see what would happen.

As luck would have it, when Tristram arrived in Ireland, a dragon was terrorizing the countryside. "What better way to impress Iseult in the name of the king and to atone for killing Moraunt than by slaying a dragon?" thought Tristram. And slay the dragon is exactly what he did.

To prove his feat, he cut the dragon's tongue out and put it in his pocket to present to the king and queen of Ireland. But he grew exhausted and promptly fell asleep. Another knight, one notorious for his cowardice, happened by, saw the slain dragon, and cut off its head. He presented this as proof to the queen that he had killed the dragon. In exchange he asked for Iseult's hand. When the queen told Iseult that this lowly knight was the slayer of the dragon, she didn't believe it.

"Come, mother," said Iseult, "let us go see this dragon ourselves. I am suspicious." They arrived at the site of the headless dragon to find Tristram just waking up.

"Tramtris!" said a surprised Iseult. "Why have you come back?"

"Why, to slay your dragon!" replied Tristram.

"*You* slew it? Someone else has already claimed that accomplishment," said the queen. "He brought us its head."

"Ah," said Tristram, pulling his hand from his pocket, "but I have the dragon's tongue. Surely a tongue without a head is more persuasive than a head without a tongue, since I must have had the head in order to get the tongue."

The queen and Iseult couldn't argue with that logic. Just as Tristram had hoped, the king and queen pardoned him for killing their son and retracted his banishment from Ireland.

"I would like to ask for one more favor," said Tristram to the king and queen. "On behalf of my king, Mark of Cornwall, I ask for your daughter's hand."

"King Mark of Cornwall?" gasped Iseult when her parents told her of the request. She had thought that Tristram had returned to woo her for himself. The king consented to the union, and though Iseult was saddened by this unexpected turn of events, she knew she must obey her father's wishes.

Though Tristram and Iseult kept their love for each other a secret, even from each other, Iseult's mother sensed the love between them. Before Iseult departed, she gave Iseult's hand-maiden, who would accompany her to Cornwall, a love potion in a silver cup.

"The union of Iseult and King Mark is a good one," said the queen to the handmaiden. "I want to be sure it lasts. Take this potion and give it to both King Mark and Iseult at their wedding feast. It will ensure their love for each other."

Foolishly, the servant left the goblet in an easily accessible cupboard aboard the ship, and as Iseult and Tristram sat talking one day, they became thirsty and happened upon it. Sharing the contents of the cup, their love grew stronger and they were unable to keep it a secret from each other any longer. But Tristram's honor to his king was equally strong, and they agreed that Iseult's marriage to King Mark should proceed.

After the wedding, Tristram and Iseult found as many excuses as they could to be together, which aroused King Mark's jealousy. To avoid bringing scandal to the court and dishonor to himself and the new queen, Tristram reluctantly decided that he must leave Cornwall. Eventually he joined King Arthur's knights of the Round Table and, hoping to forget the love of his life, married another woman named Iseult. Though he was fond of his wife, he was not in love with her, and still he pined for his first Iseult, the queen of Cornwall.

One day during a joust, Tristram was seriously wounded. He

lapsed into a delirium, during which he spoke of the first Iseult, the love of his life. His wife soon realized that she was not her husband's true love. The seed of jealousy was planted.

In a lucid moment, Tristram told his wife that the only person who could cure him was Queen Iseult of Cornwall. He requested that a ship be sent to bring her to him.

"I'm not certain she will come to my aid," said Tristram. "Tell the captain to fly a white flag on his return if Queen Iseult is with him and to fly a black flag if she is not. If you see a black flag, you will know that I am doomed." In order to save her husband's life, Iseult sent for her rival, though she had her reservations.

The day came when the ship was due back. Tristram was barely alive. "Look out the window and tell me what you see," he said to his wife. The ship was just appearing over the horizon—just a little speck, slowly growing as it neared the land. Soon the sails were in sight, billowing in the breeze, white as clouds. Atop the mast flew an equally white flag. Jealousy grew in Iseult's heart as the ship grew nearer.

"The flag is black," she lied.

"Then it is over," sighed Tristram and died.

As Queen Iseult stepped off the ship she was told the news. Quickly she ran to Tristram's side, embraced his lifeless body, and kissed his still-warm lips. Then she, too, died.

Tristram and Iseult's bodies were buried in Cornwall, side by side. A vine grew from Tristram's grave to Iseult's, where it still grows today, despite many attempts to uproot it.

The Daughter of the Sun and Moon
Ambundu/African

Kimanaweze refused to marry a woman of the earth. "When I marry," he told his father confidently, "I'll marry the daughter of the sun and moon." Kimanaweze's father didn't believe a word of it, but his son was just entering marriageable age, so he wasn't too concerned that the boy was wasting his time. But Kimanaweze was serious—he already had a plan to petition the sun for his daughter's hand.

He wrote a very polite and sincere note to Lord Sun, describing his merits, his family, and his honorable intentions regarding the sun's daughter. Next, he had to deliver it somehow. He thought that perhaps the animals, who seemed to know a lot of secrets about nature, might be able to help. First he approached a deer, and asked whether he could deliver the letter to the sun and moon.

"I'd sure like to help you, Kimanaweze," replied the deer, "but I wouldn't know the first thing about reaching the heavens, where the sun and moon's mansion lies."

Next Kimanaweze consulted an antelope and received more or less the same response. "Maybe you should ask someone who flies," said the antelope. "That's what I'd do if I were you."

So Kimanaweze brought the letter to a hawk to deliver. "I can fly high and far, son," said the hawk, "but not that high or that far. Sorry." The vulture, too, refused the assignment.

The hopeful bachelor was sitting on a stump, thinking about who might be able to deliver the marriage proposal, when a frog hopped up beside him. "I'll deliver the letter for you," said the frog.

"Don't be ridiculous," laughed Kimanaweze. "How do you expect to get into heaven? You're just teasing me."

"I have my ways, young man," responded the frog. "Trust me on this. I wouldn't tease you."

Thinking that he really had nothing to lose, the boy handed the letter to the frog, who took it and hopped off. The frog knew that the sun and moon sent their servants to a particular earthly well to fetch water every day. They traveled to and from the sky by means of a spiderweb. The next morning, before they arrived, the frog jumped into the well, holding the letter in his mouth. When the servants dipped their empty jugs into the well, the frog climbed into one of them and was carried to heaven. When he arrived, he hopped out of the jug, put the letter on the table, and then hid.

Later, Lord Sun noticed the letter and read it. "How strange," he thought. "A man from earth wants to marry our daughter." He asked everyone in the mansion whether they knew where the letter had come from, but no one had any idea. Perplexed, he put the letter away and thought no more about it. Meanwhile, the frog hopped into an empty water jug and waited for his ride back to earth the next morning.

The frog told Kimanaweze that he had delivered the letter and that Lord Sun had read it, but since several days had passed with no response, the boy was skeptical. "Write another letter," urged the frog, "and I'll deliver it again. He probably just wants to see if you're sincere."

Kimanaweze wrote the letter and the frog delivered it. Lord Sun found and read the letter, which asked for a response to the proposal, either accepting or rejecting it. Lord Sun, still puzzled, wrote back, saying, "I'll consent to the marriage, provided you come in person with your first wedding offering." The letter was delivered to Kimanaweze, who was very happy to receive it. He wrote back: "I will come once you tell me what to bring as my offering to you."

Lord Sun received the letter and told his wife, Lady Moon, that their daughter had a mysterious suitor. She was intrigued, so she prepared a nice meal and left it on the table where the letters had been found. When all was quiet in the middle of the night, the frog came out of hiding and enjoyed the meal. He also picked up a letter from Lord Sun stating that the offering he required for his daughter was a sackful of money.

It took Kimanaweze several days to collect the money, but he managed to do it, and the frog delivered it in the usual manner, along with a note that said, "Here is my initial offering. Soon I will find a way to bring home my wife." Lord Sun and Lady Moon, finding the sack of money on the table, accepted it and prepared a nice meal, which the frog ate.

The frog returned to Kimanaweze's house and told him the good news. "But how am I ever going to bring my bride home?" asked Kimanaweze. "You can carry notes, and even a sack of money, but there's no way on heaven or earth that you can bring my bride to me."

"You underestimate me," croaked the frog. "Have faith, my boy. Your bride will arrive soon."

The frog then traveled back to the mansion of the sun and moon and hid away until late at night. When all was quiet, he came out and searched the house for the daughter's bedroom. Eventually he found it and, using his magic powers, cast a spell on her, removing her eyes without waking her. He carefully wrapped the eyes in a handkerchief and hid near the water jugs.

Next morning, Lord Sun and Lady Moon were concerned that their daughter not yet awakened. They went to see her and learned that she was blind. Terribly upset, they sent for a seer to find out what they should do.

"A curse has been put on your daughter by a suitor," spoke the seer. "She will die unless you send her to him."

Lord Sun and Lady Moon, hearing this prediction, decided at once to prepare for their daughter to go to earth to meet her fiancé. "Tomorrow, we shall order Spider to weave a web large enough for our daughter to climb down to earth," said Lord Sun. The hidden frog heard this news, and the next day, when the servants carried the empty water jugs down to be filled, he stowed away. He lost no time getting to Kimanaweze's house to tell him that his bride would arrive that day.

Kimanaweze was a bit skeptical, but since the frog hadn't been wrong so far, he prepared for the arrival of his bride. Sure enough, that evening the daughter of the sun and moon was carried down to the well by means of the new spiderweb. The frog met her there, returned her eyes, and escorted her to the home of Kimanaweze. The young man and the daughter of the sun and moon were soon married, and they lived happily on earth.

SAVITRI AND SATYAVAN *Hindu*

King Asvapati should have been happy. His kingdom was at peace, the people liked and admired him, and everyone was reasonably prosperous. But one thing weighed heavily on his mind: He didn't have a son. Year after year he made offerings, prayed, and continued to live a humble life so as not to offend the gods, that they might grant him an heir.

One day, Savitri, the wife of the great god Brahma, appeared to Asvapati. "I have observed your piety and am greatly pleased. I am aware of your wishes for a male child and have consulted with Brahma. He has decreed that you shall have a daughter, whose magnificence will be unrivaled."

The king, very surprised by this auspicious visit, was even more startled by what Savitri told him. Though it seemed he was destined not to have a son, he would certainly love and accept this gift from Brahma.

Shortly thereafter, the queen conceived and gave birth to a precious girl and named her Savitri, after Brahma's wife. She grew into a fine young woman with a sensitive soul and a sharp, philosophical mind. Her physical beauty was surpassed only by her kindness and intellect. In what seemed like no time she was of age to marry, yet few suitors came to call on her.

"Savitri," her father said to her one day, "you know I want the greatest happiness for you, for you have made me happier than I could imagine. But I am concerned. The time has come for you to wed, but all the men are intimidated by your independence and your spiritual virtue. None feels worthy of you. And the few who do come, you reject."

"I have nothing against marriage, father," replied Savitri, "but I must marry for love."

"Then do so, sweet Savitri. But sometimes love doesn't come to you. You must go and seek it out yourself. So now the task falls to you to find a husband who is your equal. Only then can you avoid dishonoring yourself and your family by remaining unmarried."

So Savitri left the kingdom to search for a husband. She was gone a very long time, but the tales of her kind deeds came back to the kingdom and warmed her father's heart.

One day, she returned to the kingdom and went to her father, who was sitting in council with his adviser, the seer Narada. She stood before Asvapati, who bade her report on her search for a worthy husband.

"In a faraway kingdom," Savitri began, "lives kindly King Dyumatsena, who was struck blind. His enemies seized his kingdom and banished him and his wife and child to the woods. They live a contemplative life as hermits, and it is in these conditions that the son grew to be a man. He is sincere and pure of heart, and it is he whom I wish to marry. His name is Satyavan."

"Is he fair?" asked Savitri's father.

"He is as dependable as the seasons," replied Savitri.

"Is he intelligent?"

"Clever like the gods, but his cleverness is tempered with profound humility."

"Is he of good health?"

"He is energetic and vital, plus blessed with a handsome face."

"And you love him?" asked the king.

"My heart will forever be his," Savitri answered.

Satisfied with his daughter's sincerity, Asvapati asked Narada what he knew of the hermit-prince.

"I know of this Satyavan," said Narada softly. "A great injustice was paid to his family when his father was deposed, but all that Savitri says of him is true. His virtues are many. However, I know something else, something that Savitri couldn't know. Satyavan is fated to die within a year of his marriage."

The king turned to Savitri and said, "Do not make Satyavan's misfortune your own. Choose another husband. Choose a man who can give you many children and with whom you can grow old."

"This news is troubling, Father," replied Savitri. "But my heart has made this choice, and my mind cannot change it. My life with Satyavan may be short, but the happiness it will bring will last me all my days."

"Your words are truly from your heart, and so I consent to this marriage and give it my blessing."

So Savitri and Satyavan, as they requested, were wed in a ceremony that was more befitting two hermits than a prince and a princess. Though their garments were drab and their ceremony was simple, joy ruled the day. Still, Savitri held great sadness in the back of her mind, knowing of her husband's fate.

The young couple settled happily into their marriage and set up a humble home near Satyavan's parents, who loved Savitri dearly. The days flowed by, and the cycle of a year was almost completed. Savitri never revealed her husband's tragic destiny to him or his parents, but she adopted a holy life, endured great fasting, and made sacred offerings to the gods to show her acceptance of what fate had decreed.

All too soon, the dreaded anniversary day arrived. In honor of Savitri and Satyavan's anniversary, the hermits gathered around Savitri, who was pale from fasting and anguish, and bestowed upon her a blessing. "May you never be a widow," they prayed.

Satyavan wished to build a sacred fire to honor the day, so he picked up an ax and headed into the woods. Savitri asked if she might accompany him, and he consented, though he was concerned about her weakness from hunger. Savitri assured him that the grandeur of the forest would rejuvenate her soul and body.

The woods were spangled with flashes of light coming through the leaves. The earthy aroma of the moss and mud filled Satyavan's and Savitri's nostrils. The snapping twigs, crunching brush, and twittering birds were a symphony to their ears. "This is the last time we'll enjoy these woods together," thought Savitri. "These sights, these smells, these sounds will be among the last he experiences, and for me they'll no longer bring pleasure."

The couple was well into the woods when Satyavan selected a

great tree suitable for a sacred fire. He had been chopping at it for several minutes when suddenly he stopped, dropped his ax, and leaned against the trunk, his face entirely ashen.

"I am ill, Savitri," Satyavan groaned, barely able to speak. "My brain is on fire." He slumped down at the foot of the tree as Savitri rushed over. She put his head in her lap, stroking his hair.

"Rest now, dear," she said, blinking back her tears.

A crack of a branch caught her attention. She turned and saw the figure of a man, but he was blue-green like mold, and his eyes were deep-red glistening pools. In his hand dangled a noose.

"Who are—"

"I am Yama, lord of the dead," he whispered. "Do not be afraid, Savitri, I have no business with you. It is your husband I have come for."

With his noose, Yama tore Satyavan's soul from his body and began to carry it off, leaving Savitri holding her husband's lifeless corpse. Savitri gently laid her husband's body beneath the tree, then she rose up and shouted, "Wait!"

Yama, walking away, paused for a moment and turned his dull red eyes toward her. Then he returned to his mission.

"If your business is with my husband, it is also with me," exclaimed Savitri as she chased after Yama, "for we are as one person, each one incomplete without the other."

"Do not follow, Savitri. The world of the dead is not your world yet, for you still draw breath. Return home and prepare your husband's burial."

But Savitri continued to follow Yama. "As my husband's wife, I fulfilled every duty to the gods and to my husband. My husband has served me equally well, and together, through our love for each other, we have established a holiness and a wholeness that death cannot erase. Whether he travels of his own will or is carried off without consent, I must go with him. That is the holy law."

"Your words have merit, Savitri, but I cannot restore your husband's life. I will, however, grant any other wish you ask of me. But you must not follow me farther."

"My wish is for Satyavan's father to regain his vision and with it his kingdom."

"I grant that to you. Now return home and witness it."

But Savitri continued to follow. The woods became increasingly eerie as they walked. Less light penetrated as the foliage grew heavier and more menacing. The birds stopped singing. Then there was almost no sound at all, except for Savitri's footsteps. The realm of the dead drew nearer.

Yama once again turned to Savitri. "Go from this place! No living person is allowed to enter the realm of the dead."

"Do not the righteous deserve happiness?" asked Savitri. "Is not love the highest achievement? Why then are my happiness and my love being stolen from me?"

"Your words have truth. Again I'll grant you a wish, but not the return of Satyavan."

"My father prayed to Brahma for an heir, and I was delivered to him. I have yet to produce children, so there will be no male heir for my father. My wish is to have one hundred sons to honor my father and my husband."

"Your wish is granted, Savitri. You will have sons, and your father will have heirs. Now go!"

Savitri could faintly hear the howling of the ferocious two-headed dog that guards the entrance to the realm of the dead.

"But how can I have these sons if my husband is dead?" questioned Savitri. "To make this wish come true, you must return Satyavan to me!"

Lord Yama stopped in his tracks. Slowly, he turned and faced Savitri. "Your logic is like an arrow that reaches its mark. This, plus the fact that you have followed me as far as you have proves that you are protected by Brahma himself. You have won your husband's life. Go, return now to the woods, and you will find Satyavan asleep where you left him. You and he will live for four centuries, and then I will come for both of you." Then Yama turned away and vanished into the realm of the dead.

By the time Savitri returned to the tree, the moon was high.

She touched Satyavan's cheek and he awoke. "I have overslept, Savitri! And what a strange dream I had! Come, let us return home and begin the festivities."

When they reached their hermitage, they found a flurry of excitement. "What has happened?" Satyavan asked a sage whom they had never seen before.

"I come with news from your father's kingdom and arrive to find better news here," declared the stranger.

"Speak sense!" demanded Satyavan.

"The oppressor of your father and his kingdom has died. I was sent here to deliver to your father his rightful place as king. And when I arrived, I learned that his eyesight had been restored not an hour earlier."

Savitri and Satyavan rushed to see his father, who was able to look upon his daughter-in-law for the very first time. He was restored to the throne and ruled until his death many, many years later. Meanwhile, Savitri and Satyavan produced an abundance of heirs. The couple lived long, happy lives, and when the time came, they died peacefully together.

THE LOVE TEST *Japanese*

One day, a wealthy and powerful woman announced that she was looking for a husband. Needless to say, men flocked to her, hoping to win her hand.

"The man I marry will love me enough that he will do whatever I say," she declared. "Before I marry a man, he must prove his love and worthiness."

Many brave samurai called on the woman, willing to submit to whatever she asked. To each one she said, "If you fail this test, you must promise never to reveal anything about the test to anyone else." The samurai, bound by their honor, agreed.

Weeks went by and the samurai marched in and out, yet none passed her test. Occasionally a hopeful samurai, arriving at the woman's estate, would meet one of the failed warriors on his way out, looking ashen and horrified. But none would speak of the test he had been subjected to.

One day, an impoverished samurai arrived to take the test. He was not like the others. He was quiet and filled with none of the bravado so typical of samurai. The woman could tell that this man was different, and this difference appealed to her. They talked for a while and grew fond of each other. Daytime turned to night, and now it was time for the test to begin.

"Come with me," beckoned the woman as she left the house. The night was moonless and dark, and the hopeful husband had trouble following her. Neither one said a word. They walked for quite a distance, and when they stopped, the samurai realized that they were in a graveyard. In the dim light he could see the woman digging up one of the graves. He was disconcerted, to say the least, but he kept his resolve.

Soon the shovel made a sharp sound in the earth. The woman had uncovered a coffin. She lit a small torch, which provided just the barest amount of illumination, and without saying a word pried open the coffin lid. Inside, the samurai could see, was the body of a child. The woman, climbing down into the grave, reached down, tore off the child's arm, and began to eat it.

The samurai was shocked speechless. "Eat some!" shouted the woman, her words garbled by her chewing. Shaken, but with nothing to lose, the samurai reached into the grave, tore off the other arm, and took a bite of the hand.

"It's . . . only bread!" said the samurai, laughing and giddy with relief. "It's delicious!"

"At last I've found a brave man," the woman shouted with glee. "And, more important, one who appreciates my sense of humor!"

The two spent the rest of the night laughing, and their happiness together continued for the rest of their lives.

THE SKY MAIDEN *Algonquin/Native American*

The warrior Algon was hunting in the prairie when he noticed a strange ring worn into the grass. Wondering what might have made it, he hid behind some shrubs. He didn't have long to wait before he heard the sound of unearthly music wafting down from the sky. Looking up, he saw what first appeared to be a tiny leaf blowing high in the air. But as it drew nearer, he saw that it was a large woven basket. Inside were twelve singing sky maidens. They sang a strange but captivating song.

Concealed behind the shrubs, Algon watched as the basket touched down in the center of the circle and the maidens climbed out and began dancing around in a ring. They were all very beautiful, but Algon was particularly attracted to the youngest one, who was by far the most delicate and whose voice, at least to Algon's ear, was sweetest.

Algon sat motionless, mesmerized by the maiden. Then, finally, he could resist her no longer. He must have her for his bride, he thought. So off he dashed to grab the unsuspecting maiden. But she and her sisters were too quick; they hopped into their basket and, by singing their magical song, ascended into the sky. Algon watched in amazement as the basket rose higher and higher until it disappeared.

The young hunter was totally smitten. He returned to his lodge but could not stop thinking about his lovely sky maiden. The next day at about the same time he returned to the circle and concealed himself again. Once again he heard the captivating music. Once again the basket with the twelve sky maidens descended and the maidens got out and danced. Once again he tried to catch the youngest. And once again he failed and the sky maidens disappeared into the heavens.

Algon was more in love with the youngest sky maiden than ever. He thought of a plan. Looking around, he found a hollow tree trunk that was home to a family of mice. Early the next morning, Algon dragged the trunk over to the sky maidens' circle. Then, using magical roots from his medicine bag, he turned himself into a mouse and crawled into the trunk.

It wasn't long before the sky maidens once again came to earth in their basket. All but the youngest hopped out and began dancing in their circle. The youngest refused to leave the basket. "That tree trunk wasn't there yesterday," she told her sisters. "I don't trust it. I'll bet that mortal is somewhere about."

"Don't be silly," said the oldest sister. "Come, I'll show you." She knocked over the tree trunk and out scurried the frightened family of mice, including Algon. The sisters made a game of chasing them away. Soon all were gone except for Algon. Just as the youngest sister was about to give chase to the last mouse, the hunter regained his human form, swept her off her feet, and carried her to his lodge. It happened so quickly that the remaining sisters didn't know what to do. They fled to their basket and returned to the sky, vowing never to visit the earth again.

At first the youngest sky maiden was angry and uncooperative, but soon she realized that Algon's intentions were honorable and that he really loved her. Soon her love for him grew as well, and so the two were married. In time, they had a son and were to all appearances very happy. Secretly, however, the sky maiden missed her celestial home. In her spare time she wove a basket, and when it was complete, she entered it with her infant son. Singing a magical song, she floated up to the heavens with him. Her parents and sisters were delighted to see her after so many years, and the sky maiden was glad to be home. She tried not to think about her husband, whom she missed.

Meanwhile, Algon, bereaved over the loss of his wife and son, visited the overgrown ring site every day, hoping they would return to him. Days became years. Up in the sky, his infant son had grown into a young boy who asked his mother many difficult questions about his father. This made the sky maiden's heart ache for her husband.

"Why can't we go and visit him?" asked the child.

"Well, let's ask your grandfather if that would be a good idea," she replied.

The sky maiden consulted her father, who said, "Your husband loves you, and you love your husband. I think a visit is called for. He deserves to see how well his son has turned out. Why don't you bring Algon back here with you and ask him to bring a part from every beast that crawls or flies or swims on the earth as gifts for our people. It's time we learned more about these mortals."

With her father's blessing, the sky maiden and her son returned to earth in their basket. Algon was at the site of the dancing circle when they arrived and was elated to be reunited with them. He readily agreed to return with them to the sky people, and he worked long and hard collecting remnants of every animal he could find—claws and feathers, fur and scales, beaks and tails, paws and fins. Finally, he had them all, and he and his family climbed into the basket and soared skyward.

When they arrived in the land of the sky people, the citizens greeted them with great fanfare. The sky maiden's father began to distribute the gifts that Algon had brought. As each sky person took an animal part, he or she was transformed into that animal. Algon selected three white feathers for himself, his wife, and their son. They were instantly transformed into a family of white falcons and were able to fly between the sky world and the earthly world. To this day, their descendants swoop and soar over the prairies and woods.

4

NATURE

THE NATURAL WORLD HAS ALWAYS HELD amazing wonders for humans—day and night, summer and winter, thunder and lightning, life and death. Natural phenomena were especially powerful and magical to early civilizations. They attributed these wonders to the gods, the creators. In their generosity they bestowed great gifts upon the earth, granting humans cultivation and prosperity. But, at times, the gods became angry at humans and as punishment unleashed their fury on the earth by way of storms, famine, or drought.

From the beginning of time, humans have struggled to gain control over such forces of nature. Consider fire: As a gift from the gods, humans learned to harness fire. It became a civilizing force, making life more comfortable with warmth and light. But even today fire remains unpredictable and, at times, reminds humans that the gods have ultimate control over it.

While humans warmed themselves fireside, animals also had gifts from the gods to savor, such as flight and rejuvenation. Humans saw that animals had a secret world of their own, where they interacted in complex ways and exhibited their magical powers. Wise humans learned from animals, realizing that they could be friends or enemies, helpers or tricksters.

The magical stories here describe how ancient people came to understand or harness the natural phenomena they encountered every day. They illustrate the unique and often problematic relationships animals share with humans and with one another. Ultimately, they represent ancient cultures' explanations of how the natural world came to be.

THE TASK OF PROMETHEUS
AND EPIMETHEUS *Greek*

After the gods of Mount Olympus defeated the Titans, they began to organize the earth. First, Zeus and his brothers divided their domain. Zeus ruled the heavens, Poseidon ruled the sea, and Hades reigned in the underworld. To send messages to his brothers, Zeus would dispatch couriers. One of these was Iris, who took the form of a rainbow and often ran errands for Zeus' wife, Hera.

Prometheus and Epimetheus, two Titans who had sided with the gods in the battle for supremacy, were not without their jobs to do. Zeus entrusted them with the task of creating human beings and the animals. Prometheus, whose name means "forethought," was much brighter than his feeble-minded brother, Epimetheus, whose name means "afterthought."

"Epimetheus," said Prometheus, "I have been given the task of creating humans, so I am going to be very busy. Meanwhile, Zeus wants to fill the world with other creatures. I will leave it to you to shape them and to decide their nature."

"You can count on me, brother! I cannot wait to get started," Epimetheus said eagerly.

"Now, remember," warned Prometheus as he handed his brother a sack, "these are the qualities you have to work with. Use them wisely and *sparingly*. Save something special for the humans I am going to create."

Prometheus went on his way to mull over the design of humans. His brother untied the sack and marveled at its contents. Inside he saw hard shells and downy feathers, sharp fangs and long claws, shiny scales and colorful furs, elegant whiskers and serious quills, pointy beaks and various tongues, matching sets of paws and pairs of fins, and all manner of other things.

Epimetheus was thrilled beyond belief. At once he set about

combining these qualities to create the animals. And before he knew it, the sack was empty.

Meanwhile, Prometheus was shaping man from clay and water. "How many legs?" he wondered. "Four? Six? Perhaps eight." He molded and remolded the clay, unhappy with the results. Finally, an idea struck him. "If humans are to be the supreme animal, then they should resemble the gods." And so Prometheus shaped a human with two legs and two arms. Proud of his sculpture, he presented it grandly to Athena, the goddess of wisdom, who breathed life and soul into it.

Prometheus took his creation to his brother to see what special qualities he could give to the humans. When Epimetheus told him that he had used up all the gifts on the animals, Prometheus was furious.

"You dolt!" he shouted. "The humans were to be my crowning creation. Now they're doomed to be ordinary, separated from the animals only by their upright posture, but otherwise unremarkable."

But the ability to walk upright proved to be an advantage after all. It allowed humans to work with their hands, make tools, and build crude shelters.

Still disappointed by the humans' lack of more special qualities, Prometheus was nonetheless extremely proud of his creation. In fact, he began to favor the humans over the gods. The gods, meanwhile, saw the humans as beings designed to worship them—since they looked like gods—and they began to discuss what parts of sacrificial animals should be given to the gods and what parts the humans should keep for themselves. They agreed to let Zeus decide.

Prometheus wanted his creation to have the best of everything, so he devised a plan to trick Zeus into choosing the less desirable parts of animals for the gods. He volunteered to slaughter an ox and divide it into two offerings. On one plate he put the flesh and most of the other desirable parts, then he covered them with some bones and gristle. On the other plate he piled most of the bones, but he concealed them with a small portion of tempting fat and meat. Zeus chose the plate that appeared to have the most meat but which in fact held mostly bones. He was furious at being tricked, and he promised to punish the humans.

"Let them have this meat!" declared a red-faced Zeus. "But they'll have to eat it raw. I forbid them to use fire!"

Without fire, the humans couldn't progress much further than they had already come. Zeus' prohibition disturbed Prometheus. "If humankind is supposed to be the gods' best effort, then humans should have more tools," he thought. There was no question about it, fire was essential to humans. Prometheus was determined to deliver it.

He talked Athena into lifting him toward the heavens, where he visited the chariot of the sun. He touched a fennel stalk to the chariot's wheel until it started to burn, and he smuggled this spark to earth. It was not long before the smell of burning sacrifices reached Zeus' nostrils. Looking down on earth, he was livid to see that humans had forged strong tools, built many great cities, and advanced themselves with the blessing of fire.

For his crime, Prometheus earned one of Zeus' cruellest punishments. Zeus commanded his blacksmith, Hephaestus, to forge unbreakable chains. With these chains, Prometheus was bound and tied to the crest of a mountain, where each day a huge eagle, endowed with the features Epimetheus had given it, swooped down and ate Prometheus' liver. Because Prometheus was immortal, he would survive the agonizing ordeal and his liver would grow back each night, only to be eaten by the eagle again the following day.

The Abduction of Persephone *Greek*

Demeter, the goddess of agriculture, was responsible for all the world's plant life, but the prize fruit of her labor was her daughter by Zeus, Persephone. Young Persephone was gentle and happy, and she loved the bountiful flowers and plants that sprang from the earth. Persephone was the delight of all the gods. Her nature was so innocent that even Hera, Zeus' wife, couldn't harbor jealousy for her husband's illegitimate daughter.

Hades, Zeus' brother and the god of the underworld, was lonely. He was a powerful ruler in a bleak and dismal place and was disheartened by his solitude. One day, as he was traveling to Olympus, he spied Persephone frolicking in a field and lost his heart to her. He immediately called on Zeus to ask permission to marry her.

"You know I have a thankless job in a joyless place," argued Hades. "Why not indulge me in the delight of your beautiful daughter's hand?"

"My brother," said Zeus, "you will have no argument from me. It is only by fate that you rule the underworld and I rule Mount Olympus. After all, it could easily have been the other way around. Persephone deserves to marry none other than a powerful ruler. You qualify, and I know your love for her is genuine. I consent to your union—"

"Thank you!" interrupted Hades in his joy.

"But there is one problem," Zeus continued. "Persephone's mother, Demeter. There is no way she would allow it. To her, Persephone is the essence of all that is alive. She would not like the idea of her daughter as queen of the dead."

"I see your point," said Hades, frowning.

"So let's just not tell her. I will deal with the consequences. The gods know, I have had lots of experience dealing with difficult

goddesses!" The two brothers embraced, and then Hades returned
to the underworld a happy god.

The next day, Persephone and her friends were in a field collecting wildflowers. They giggled and joked under the bright blue
sky, making a contest out of finding the greatest variety of blossoms. As Persephone gathered her flowers, a bright flash of color
at the far end of the field caught her eye. Intrigued, she went to
investigate. As she drew near, she saw it was a flower whose petals
were different from any she had ever seen. She looked around for
others, but only that one blossom grew. Delighted, she plucked it
and put it to her nose to enjoy its aroma.

Suddenly the ground shook and the earth split open before
her. The stunned goddess had no time to run or even think about
what was happening before Hades burst from the ground in his
speeding chariot, grabbed her, and disappeared back into the earth.
Persephone's spilled flower basket was the only trace of her that
remained. Her friends, having wandered over a hill and out of
sight, witnessed nothing.

Persephone was gone, and Demeter was frantic. She combed
the earth searching for her daughter but could find not a sign.
Despondent, she sat on a boulder grieving for nine long days and
nights. The burning sun, the pouring rain, hunger, thirst—
Demeter was numb to all. Her grief soon turned to anger.

"All the earth should know my loss!" declared the goddess.
"From now on, the ground will no longer nurture seeds. Trees will
wither and grain shall rot."

And so it was. Famine choked the earth. Livestock starved,
and soon people were also dying of hunger. Zeus, fearing the
destruction of all he had worked for, realized that Persephone must
return to Demeter. Meanwhile, Persephone, on her throne next to
Hades in the dismal land of the dead, tried to accept her sad fate.
Her husband treated her with respect and kindness. He provided
her with all he could to make her comfortable. Elegant meals were
set before her, but she wouldn't touch a morsel. Servants waited to
attend to her every need, but she asked for nothing. What she

craved was not available where the dead dwelled: sunlight, flowers, and her mother.

Zeus sent his friend Hermes, the messenger god, to fetch Persephone, figuring that Hades would understand the situation. Hermes arrived to find Persephone sitting stolidly, blankly staring into space.

"Greetings, Persephone and Hades," began Hermes. "I come on an errand for Zeus."

"Salutations, Hermes," replied Hades, "What is the nature of your errand?"

"The earth is dying. Plants refuse to grow and seeds spoil in the dirt. The goddess Demeter is punishing the world for the loss of Persephone."

Hearing her mother's name, Persephone snapped out of her gloomy reverie.

"My mother," said Persephone. "Is she all right?"

"She misses you very much, and she is willing to destroy all life on earth if that is what it takes to win your return."

Persephone turned to her husband. "Don't you see, I must go back! Mother's will is not easily swayed."

"I love you, Persephone," replied Hades, taking her hand, "but I see that you're not happy here, nor will you ever be. The burden of your unhappiness weighs on me more than the end of life on earth. Go, then. Return to your world of flowers and light. Be well, but think of me and know that I love you."

They embraced and kissed good-bye. Then, as Persephone turned to leave, Hades said: "The journey back to the land of the living is long, and you haven't eaten the whole time you have been here. You need something to fortify you for your trip." He handed her a few pomegranate seeds, luscious and ripe. She put them in her mouth, then took Hermes' hand and began her ascent.

Hermes delivered Persephone to the hall of Zeus, where Demeter sat waiting impatiently. She jumped up when she saw Persephone, and mother and daughter hugged and cried and kissed. The pair went to earth to walk the fields and meadows.

Wherever they stepped, the brown, burned grasses turned green and lush, flowers bloomed, and life returned to the soil. Demeter's happiness spread quickly, and soon the earth flourished again. The goddess and her daughter talked about their ordeals.

"I could neither eat nor sleep from worry over what had become of you," Demeter said.

"And I felt the same way, for missing you," said Persephone. "Though lavish foods were prepared for me in the underworld, I wanted not a single bite."

"It's better that way, dear daughter. The food of the dead is not for the living. If a living person partakes of food in the realm of the dead, she is doomed to remain there."

"Well, I ate noth—Oh dear!" gasped Persephone. "I *did* eat a few pomegranate seeds just to sustain me on my return to you."

"But that is enough!" cried Demeter, very upset. "The law is clear. Persephone, I fear I have lost you, but I refuse to let you go. I will return to Zeus and beg for an appeal."

Demeter presented herself before Zeus and explained the situation. "You know my wrath," she said. "If Persephone must endure the underworld, then the earth must endure the death of its fields and forests."

"We all will miss Persephone," Zeus replied, "but even I can't change the law. Once food is eaten in Hades' kingdom, a person must stay there. I may be able to reach a compromise as long as you and Hades agree. Here is my offer: Because Persephone's infraction amounts to only a few pomegranate seeds, let her stay in Hades for a short time each year—three months. The rest of the year she can frolic in the land of the living."

"I suppose that is fair," said Demeter. "It pains me to think of my daughter in that awful place, though, and I will not withdraw my threat. For each day Persephone is in the underworld, plants will die on earth. When she returns, life will be restored."

So it came to pass that when Persephone spends her three months with Hades, winter shrouds the earth. When she returns, she brings the first blossoms of spring.

GILGAMESH'S QUEST FOR IMMORTALITY
Babylonian

After defeating the monster Humbaba in the sacred forest of the gods and insulting the goddess Ishtar, Gilgamesh and Enkidu—friends and warriors equal in strength and intelligence—were honored by their people as heroes. But their long-sought happiness was short-lived. Ishtar's revenge for Gilgamesh's insolence was ruthless. The greatest, most painful punishment she could dream up for Gilgamesh was to inflict sickness on Enkidu, who became ill for the first time in his life. Over twelve days he grew weaker and weaker, quickly wasting away. No amount of magic or medicine could help him. On the thirteenth day Enkidu died.

"Dear brother," cried Gilgamesh over Enkidu's body, "we have fought so many obstacles and yet you endured. Now, for the sake of a selfish goddess's wounded pride, you wither and die an unheroic death. It seems so pointless."

Having lost his best friend, Gilgamesh felt a sense of his own mortality, and with it came his first stirring of fear. Feeling suddenly less heroic, Gilgamesh realized that the only battle that really mattered was the battle against death.

"There must be a way to defy death, to become immortal like the gods," he thought. "I must go and find that secret." Gilgamesh faced hazards that would terrify any other person, but his fear of death was so profound that nothing else compared to it. At each juncture in his quest for immortality, he was told that mortality is the nature of life, and that nothing could change it.

Unable to accept that answer, Gilgamesh set off to find a humble man named Utnapishtim, whom the gods had once entrusted with saving the creatures and plants of the earth from a devastating flood. For his good work, the gods had granted him and his wife immortality, as long as they lived in solitude. After a long and harrowing journey, Gilgamesh reached the home of Utnapishtim.

"The gift of immortality was bestowed only upon me and my wife," explained Utnapishtim. "It will never be bestowed again. But believe me—it is not so great. There's only so much that people can do before they get bored. Cherish your life while you have it."

"I cannot accept that!" cried Gilgamesh. "There must be some way to avoid death."

"Listen," replied Utnapishtim, "if you really desire to live forever, the first thing you have to do is stay awake for a week. That is the first step. Try that."

Gilgamesh laughed. "That is easy," he said. "I am certainly stronger than sleep." But the great man-god, defeater of monsters, performer of heroic deeds, eventually nodded off. Seven days later, Utnapishtim tapped him on the shoulder.

"Oh Utnapishtim! I had just nodded off when you awakened me," said Gilgamesh sleepily.

"I think not, son," said Utnapishtim, smiling. "Look at the loaves of bread beside you. My wife put one loaf there for each day you slept."

Gilgamesh looked beside him and saw seven loaves, ranging from rock-hard to moldy to still warm.

"If you cannot defeat sleep, how can you defeat death?" said Utnapishtim with a chuckle. "I hope you are now convinced that you cannot be immortal. However, there's a plant at the bottom of the sea that can restore your youth. You'll still be mortal, but you will never grow old."

"It's a start," admitted Gilgamesh. "Please tell me where I can find this plant." Utnapishtim complied.

Gilgamesh bade good-bye to his host and went off on another laborious journey to find the plant of rejuvenation. When he arrived at his destination, Gilgamesh tied rocks to his feet and plunged into the ocean to harvest the plant that grew at the bottom. Down and down he went. He was on the brink of death when he reached the bottom, but he managed to grab a small handful of the plant and untie the rocks from his feet.

Bursting through the surface of the water, Gilgamesh gulped the air and swam to the shore. Invigorated by his accomplishment, he began the long journey home. As he neared his home, he pulled the plant out of his pocket, ready to eat it. But suddenly he was overcome by fatigue. He lay on the ground and quickly fell into a deep sleep. The rejuvenating plant fell from his hands and was eaten by a passing snake.

When Gilgamesh awoke and realized what had happened, he sadly resigned himself to his fate and realized that aging and death are the way of nature. Snakes, on the other hand, gained the ability to rejuvenate themselves by shedding their skins.

Why Sun and Moon Are in the Sky

Ibibio/African

Sun and his wife, Moon, were friends of Water. All three lived on the ground. Sun would visit Water and stay all day while Moon took care of their children, Stars. Then Moon would come along later. After many, many enjoyable visits, Sun began to feel that he was imposing on Water's hospitality.

"My dear Water," said Sun, "all these years my wife and I have enjoyed coming to your home and never once have we invited you to ours. I feel just terrible about this."

"Oh, it is no matter," shrugged Water. "I don't mind at all. Besides—and don't be offended by this—your house is too small. I am very big, you know."

"If the size of our home is the only thing keeping us from being good hosts, then I will build a bigger one," Sun responded. "Moon and I were talking about that anyway."

"It would have to be quite large," warned Water.

"It will be," Sun assured him.

"I mean *really* big," suggested Water. "Huge, in fact."

"Fine," agreed cheerful Sun.

So Sun and Moon built their big, new home. When it was finished, they invited Water in to see it.

"Are you sure it is all right to enter?" asked Water, pausing outside the magnificent front door.

"Sure!" beamed Sun. "Make yourself at home!"

Water began to flow into the house, along with all the fish and snails and other creatures that lived with him. In no time he covered the floor of the house, even though he was barely through the door. In a flash he was ankle-deep, then knee-deep.

"Do you still want me to come in?" he asked.

"Oh, yes!" said Moon. "You are our guest of honor."

In Water flowed. Waist-deep. Neck-deep. Yet he had barely crossed the threshold.

"There is still a lot more of me outside," said Water, as he continued streaming in.

"Come on, come on!" insisted Sun. "You haven't seen the upstairs yet."

Water continued to flow into the house, and soon Sun and Moon had no place to stand except on the roof. But being a generous host, Sun still encouraged his friend to join the housewarming.

The flowing water covered the roof and kept going. Sun and Moon, without a dry place to stand, gathered their children and rose into the sky. And there they have lived ever since.

THE SUN GODDESS HIDES *Japanese*

Amaterasu, the sun goddess, and her brother, Tsukiyomi, the moon god, once ruled over the sky side by side. But one day they had a falling out, and that's why the moon and the sun turn their backs on each other.

The problem started when Amaterasu sent Tsukiyomi to supervise the food goddess, Ukemochi, at her work Ukemochi received the handsome Tsukiyomi very graciously and invited him to dine with her. The moon god accepted, but thought it peculiar that not a morsel of food was in sight.

"Come with me," said Ukemochi. "I am about to make dinner."

Tsukiyomi followed her to a field. There, the food goddess opened her mouth and spit out piles of boiled rice. Tsukiyomi was speechless at this sight. Then Ukemochi turned toward the sea, and all sorts of edible fish and crabs and sea plants spewed from her mouth, much to the distress of the moon god. Last, the food goddess faced the woodlands, and from her lips sprang a menagerie of furry creatures, from moose to mice.

"Dinner is served," declared Ukemochi proudly, delicately wiping her mouth.

"That's the most disgusting display I have ever seen!" shouted Tsukiyomi, looking a little green. "How do you dare serve me food that you have vomited up? I cannot think of a greater insult than this!" In his rage, Tsukiyomi struck Ukemochi dead.

When Tsukiyomi returned to heaven to tell his sister what had happened, Amaterasu was livid. "How could you have killed the food goddess? She was only doing her job. For a moon god, Tsukiyomi, sometimes you are not very bright. What you have done is unforgivable. I never want to see you again." With that, Amaterasu turned her back on her brother, and that is why you rarely see the sun and the moon in the sky at the same time.

After her disagreement with her brother, Amaterasu came down to earth to inspect the damage he had caused. She found Ukemochi's body, which continued to grow food even after death. Cattle and horses sprang from her head, silkworms from her eyebrows, grains and beans sprouted from all over her body. Amaterasu harvested this bounty and later taught people how to cultivate it and eat it.

Amaterasu had another troublesome brother, Susano-o, the storm god. Though sometimes he could be very calm, he was prone to sudden rages. His temper would flare for no reason, and he would become unpredictable and destructive. Consequently, nobody really wanted to spend any time with him, for fear of what he might do. While Amaterasu and Tsukiyomi were given the heavens as their domain, Susano-o was assigned the underworld. Not really wanting to go to such a dark place, Susano-o begged his father to let him go into the sky to say good-bye to his lovely sister before he disappeared into the realm of darkness. Reluctantly, his father agreed.

Up in the sky, Amaterasu was combing her hair and beaming upon the earth when she heard some terrible, thunderous booms and crashes. "Here comes trouble," she thought, "and his name is Susano-o." Hoping to discourage her brother's visit, she put on a quiver stocked with fifteen hundred arrows and took up her sword. With any luck, her formidable appearance would prevent her pesky brother from staying.

Soon Susano-o arrived, amid howling winds, flashing light, and intolerably loud thunder. "Hello, Sister!" boomed Susano-o. "What's with the weaponry? Expecting a battle?"

"It never hurts to be prepared," replied the sun goddess. "You never know who might turn up uninvited."

"If you are worried about me, don't be! I won't stay long. I just want to say farewell before I go to the underworld." Susano-o eventually managed to reassure his sister, and they pledged to respect each other. To seal their pledge, Susano-o gave Amaterasu a sword. Amaterasu broke it into three pieces, chewed each piece, and sprayed a fine mist from her mouth, creating three goddesses. She then gave to Susano-o her pearl necklace, which Susano-o chewed up to create eight gods. Amaterasu claimed that these gods were related to her, since they came from her own pearls. They were the ancestors of the imperial family and the seven most noble Japanese clans.

Susano-o behaved himself, at least for a while. But it wasn't long before he overstayed his welcome in heaven. He was jealous of his sister's knack for gardening, and so he repeatedly destroyed her gardens. Amaterasu remained tolerant, as was her nature, and hoped her brother would grow bored and go away.

Amaterasu was too optimistic. By ignoring her brother, she only incited him to escalate his misbehavior. He defiled her temple and the harvest of first fruits by covering everything with filth. Still, Amaterasu displayed godlike restraint. Finally, Susano-o thought of an antic that incited his sister's anger.

One day, as Amaterasu sat weaving sacred cloth for the gods' ceremonies, Susano-o stole one of heaven's colts, skinned it, and dropped it through her roof. Startled, then disgusted, Amaterasu flew into a rage. "I cannot stand any more of this!" she screamed. She ran and hid in a cave, refusing to come out.

Without Amaterasu, both heaven and earth were plunged into darkness and coldness. Plants stopped growing, work halted. The universe held its breath, wondering when the sun would shine and bring its warmth again. The gods of evil, who thrive in the dark, took advantage of the opportunity and expanded their territory across the face of the earth. Their numbers increased and so did their evil.

The benevolent gods punished Susano-o for offending the sun goddess. They cut off his beard and banished him to the oceans of earth for all eternity. But what to do about Amaterasu? How to coax her out of her cave?

The gods concocted an ingenious plan. First they hung a mirror outside the entrance of the cave. Then they gathered round, making a festive racket. A goddess performed an obscene and hilarious dance, and the heavens rang with laughter. Amaterasu, hearing the fun, wondered what was going on. "How can the gods be enjoying themselves without the benefit of my light and warmth? Could a new goddess have replaced me?" she asked herself.

Amaterasu's curiosity got the best of her. She peeked out of the cave, very cautiously. She was met with her own reflection. Intrigued, she crept ever closer and, without even realizing it, was soon out of the cave altogether. A god waiting by the mouth of the cave sealed it closed so Amaterasu could not reenter. When Amaterasu realized what was happening, she became angry. But when she learned that her brother had been severely punished, she was reassured. So Amaterasu emerged into the world once again, banishing the evil and darkness. And as long as she is respected, goodness, light, and life will prevail.

MAUI MAKES HIS MARK *Polynesian*

In the early days, the sky was so close to the earth that people were forced to hunch over to avoid hitting their heads on it. Maui, a trickster god, decided to do something about the situation. One day, while he was out making mischief with his magic, a beautiful woman caught his eye. She was carrying a bundle and, like most people, was stooped over to keep her head from banging into the sky. To impress her, Maui took a large stick and raised the sky. It has stayed where he pushed it ever since.

In raising the sky, Maui realized the effect his power could have on the world. So he decided to make the days last longer, since he enjoyed the daylight more than the night.

"Do you not think the sun travels across the sky far too quickly?" he asked his brothers.

"Sure, but there's no sense complaining about things you cannot change," replied his oldest brother.

"I'll bet I can slow the sun down," boasted Maui. "After all, I raised the sky."

"And how do you plan to do it?" asked his second brother.

"First we will have to capture the sun in a big net. I will need all of you to help me," said Maui. The brothers reluctantly agreed. They built a huge net and carried it to the east, where the sun rose each morning. They laid it out in the sun's path, each brother holding tightly to ropes on each corner. Patiently, they waited there until the first rosy glimmer of light appeared at the earth's edge.

"Here comes the sun!" whispered Maui, excitedly. "Hold tight and wait until it is completely in the net, then pull on the ropes as hard as you can."

Very soon, the sun slipped over the horizon. Before it knew what was happening, it was entangled in the net and straining against it. Maui's brothers pulled the net tight with all their might and yanked the sun down onto the ground. The sun struggled and writhed but could not break free. When it finally exhausted itself, Maui and his brothers set it free. It was so weak from its ordeal that from then on it would only crawl slowly across the sky in its daily journey.

This act was very impressive, but perhaps Maui's most important task was giving humans the ability to make fire. People had fire, but they couldn't make it themselves. They had to wait for lightning to strike.

"Since fire is so important," thought Maui, "people should have the ability to make it themselves." He immediately formed a plan. First, when everyone in the world was asleep, he went around and put out all the fires. Then he went to the underworld to visit his great-grandmother, Mahui-ike, who was the keeper of fire.

"Mahui-ike," said Maui, "the fires up above have all gone out. Can you give me some to take back?"

"Certainly, my boy," she replied, handing him one of her flaming fingernails, which is where she kept the fire.

Maui took the burning fingernail, and as soon as he was out of Mahui-ike's sight, he blew it out. Returning to her, he sheepishly said, "Grandmother, I am afraid the fire blew out before I could bring it to the upper world."

"Foolish child, you must be more careful with my gifts. Here is some more," she said, handing him another flaming nail. "Mind it closely."

Maui took it and once again blew it out as soon as he left Mahui-ike's sight. He repeated this ploy over and over again. His grandmother admonished him more strongly each time, yet she never denied him another fiery fingernail. Finally, when she was down to one last fingernail, Mahui-ike caught on to the trick.

"You want fire?" shrieked Mahui-ike in rage when Maui returned for the tenth time. "Here is your fire!" She threw the flaming fingernail at Maui. It burst into a huge fire before him. He turned to run from it, but it followed him, hot on his heels, all the way to the upper world. The whole world then caught fire, and the singed and scorched Maui had no place to run. He prayed to his father, the god Rangi, who sent down torrents of rain, which quenched the fires. But deep within the trees, sparks of the fires remained, and from then on people had the power to make their own fire by rubbing sticks together to coax it out of the wood.

Maui's last great act was for a noble purpose, but in carrying it out he met with ultimate failure.

Having learned that everyone must die, he was determined to conquer death and bring immortality to earth. Accompanied by birds, he traveled once again to the underworld, this time to sneak inside Hine, the goddess of death, as she slept with her mouth agape. As Maui approached the goddess, he said to the birds nearby, "Be very quiet. I must slip inside Hine without awakening her. If she awakens while I'm inside her, she'll kill me."

The birds agreed to be silent. They watched as Maui climbed into the goddess's mouth and slipped slowly inside her. He was almost completely in when one little bird, a wagtail, giggled at the spectacle of Maui sticking halfway out of the goddess's mouth. The bird's merry chirp awakened the goddess, who crushed Maui between her teeth, killing him and depriving humans of immortality.

Glooskap Catches Summer
Algonquin/Native American

Glooskap, the creator god, once traveled north to the Ice Country. The journey was long and cold, and Glooskap was exhausted. The landscape was bare and white except for one small wigwam, which belonged to a giant called Winter.

"Come in, come in," beckoned Winter as Glooskap approached the entrance. "Let me fix you a pipe and some food."

Winter proved to be a charming, gracious host who amused Glooskap with mystical stories of strange places and exotic creatures. As Winter spun these tales, Glooskap grew drowsier and drowsier, for in reality the giant was casting a spell on him. Glooskap fell into a heavy sleep that lasted for six months. While he slept the earth slept, too. Eventually, Glooskap's own magic broke the hold of Winter's spell, and Glooskap awoke. Still drowsy, he thanked his host for his hospitality and bade him farewell.

Glooskap then journeyed south, well past his home. Ice and snow hugged the ground. Plants hid in the earth, trying to find warmth. The farther south he went, the warmer the weather became. In a while, grass poked out of the ground. A little farther on, flowers blossomed. As he traveled farther, Glooskap came to a vast, endless forest. Beneath the tremendous trees danced a race of tiny people, the People of Light. Their beautiful queen was named Summer. As soon as Glooskap saw her, he grabbed her in his large fist and carried her off. The People of Light gave chase, but they couldn't keep up with him, and he soon left them far behind.

Glooskap concealed Summer in his vest and once again made the long trek to the Ice Country. Once again Winter greeted him graciously, and once again the giant began to weave his spell of slumber on Glooskap. But before he could get too far along, Glooskap interrupted him.

"I have a tale to tell you," spoke the god. "It is a tale of the People of Light who live in a great forest, though they themselves are smaller than my thumb."

"Is it getting warm in here?" asked the giant, starting to sweat and feel distressed.

"These tiny people hold festive ceremonies where they dance all night," said Glooskap, ignoring the giant. As Glooskap spoke, Summer released her warmth into the room. The longer Glooskap spoke, the warmer it became. Soon it was more than Winter could bear, and he headed farther north. Meanwhile, Summer's warmth melted all the ice and awakened the plants that lay dormant beneath the frozen earth. Rivers once clogged with ice now flowed freely to the ocean, and the Ice Country was alive and fragrant.

The People of Light, meanwhile, still pursuing their kidnapped queen, followed the growing warmth to Winter's wigwam. Once they found Summer, they decided to stay there, at least for a while.

"Your warmth is good," declared Glooskap to Summer. "It should be spread throughout the world so that all may benefit."

"But my people are so small in size and number," replied Summer, "and the world is so huge."

"Wherever you go, you spread warmth, just as Winter spreads his icy spell wherever he settles. If you were to pursue the Winter around the earth, then all of creation can enjoy your warmth for at least part of the year."

Summer agreed that this was a good plan, and so she gathered the People of Light and traveled north in pursuit of Winter. And that's how winter passes into summer year after year.

SEDNA OF THE SEA *Inuit/Native American*

Once there lived a young woman named Sedna who refused to get married.

"This is very unusual," said her father. "You must find a husband. You cannot spend your days just playing among the animals."

But Sedna paid no attention.

One day, a stranger came to Sedna's village. Sedna thought he was the most handsome man she had ever seen. He took a fancy to her as well. He promised Sedna all manner of luxuries.

"If you marry me, I will take you to live among my people," he told her, "and there I will spoil you with rich foods, beautiful jewels, and fine clothing."

"Will you make me work hard all the rest of my days?" asked Sedna cautiously.

"If you promise to marry me, I will give you a life of leisure. You will never have to lift a finger."

"This sounds like something I could get used to," said Sedna.

"Then you swear you will marry me?"

"Yes. I swear I will marry you."

Soon after Sedna became the bride of the handsome stranger. Everybody was very happy. After the ceremony, Sedna packed her few belongings and went with her new husband to his village.

But Sedna's husband had a secret he was keeping from his bride. The truth was that he wasn't a man at all. He was really a bird! When Sedna realized this, it did not make her happy, and although her husband kept his promise of providing a comfortable life for his wife, his birdlike standards of luxury were much different than Sedna's human standards. She was, in a word, miserable.

The days passed to months. Sedna's parents hadn't heard any news of their daughter, so her father set off to visit her and her husband. When he found her, he saw that she was clearly very unhappy with her new life. He decided to rescue his daughter and take her back home.

He hid until the morning, when most of the birds were out looking for food. Then he sneaked over to Sedna and whispered, "Come with me. I am taking you home."

"Oh, Father! I am so glad you are here!" said Sedna, with tears in her eyes.

The two made it to her father's kayak and paddled off. But while they were at sea, the sky grew black as night and the ocean churned and boiled. Rain poured down in sheets. Both Sedna and her father knew that they were doomed.

"The gods are angry at us for breaking the marriage pact," cried Sedna, though her father could barely hear her through the shrieking winds.

"We must appease them somehow," he thought. Sedna's father showed his true loyalty to the gods: to placate them, he sacrificed Sedna by throwing her overboard.

Sedna, tossing about in the icy sea, grabbed hold of her father's boat. Her father—by will of the gods—took out his knife and cut off her fingers joint by joint. The severed joints fell into the sea and became seals, walruses, sea otters, and whales.

Unable to hang on, Sedna sank. Down and down she went to the bottom of the sea, where she dwells as master of the underworld and of all the sea life.

As you might imagine after all she's been through, Sedna has a fiery temper. If she is angered, she can deprive fishermen of their catches or raise a tempest to capsize their boats. In her anger, Sedna's hair becomes tangled and matted and traps the sea animals, but since she has no fingers, she is unable to comb her hair and free them. Only a holy man, a shaman, can communicate with Sedna and soothe her. By singing mystical chants, he is able to remove his spirit from his body so that it can plunge into the depths of the ocean and meet with Sedna. There he soothes her anger and fixes her hair, thus freeing the sea creatures so they may fill the fishermen's nets again.

5

GOOD AND EVIL

THE WORLD IS FULL OF SWEET DELIGHTS, but it also holds nasty surprises that lie beyond human control. While philosophers have pondered the origin of the universe, asking "why?", the common man or woman often has posed a more immediate question: "Why *me*?"

Why do things go wrong? Why do the gods allow disease, poverty, crime? Why is no one immune to the world's evils? If the gods are all-powerful, why is the world so far from perfect? Myths were created to explain such contradictions.

In most cultures, people believe that they are able to chose between good and evil. Most people choose the path of righteousness, believing that if they treat others fairly and compassionately, others will treat them in the same way and the gods will find favor with them. This is the keystone of civilization. Without the belief that good begets good, society could never develop. Along with the precept of goodness comes the idea that the gods are for, not against, humankind, and that they ultimately want mortals to succeed. Human success and growth are the result of the gods' benevolence and the wise choices that people make.

But even so, bad things sometimes happen to good people. How can this unwarranted malice be explained? And why does evil exist in the first place? Mythology tries to answer these questions. In some cultures, evil is seen as a punishment to mortals for their disobedience to the gods—though the gods granted humans the freedom of choice, sometimes they disagree with the choices made. Evil can also be seen as the work of a separate, powerful god who lives in opposition to the creator god.

In addition, evil can be a basic part of creation, the dark side of the creator. In many Native American myths, the creator is also a trickster who can't resist pranks and practical jokes. How better to make sense of the absurd and random problems that plague humankind than through the creation of a figure that mirrors the complexity of human nature itself?

The Chinese developed the idea of yin and yang, the balancing forces of the universe. Yin is dark, negative, and female; yang is light, positive, and male. But in Eastern philosophy, *dark* and *negative* aren't synonymous with evil, just as *light* and *positive* don't necessarily mean good. These opposing forces allow the universe to function. Both forces are required for universal harmony, and bad things occur as a result of an imbalance between yin and yang. Evil isn't the absence of good; it's part of the universal fabric.

So, despite the human desire to live well and act well, to choose good over evil, bad things will still happen. The following myths and legends attempt to explain why.

PANDORA'S BOX *Greek*

When Prometheus defied Zeus' orders and gave fire to humans, they had greater control of their environment. Possession of fire had made humans much more like the gods, and Zeus felt threatened. After punishing Prometheus, Zeus cooked up a sinister, long-range plan for humankind, hoping to burden the humans with evil before they became too powerful.

Zeus visited his craftsman, Hephaestus, to enlist his help.

"I want you to create a woman as beautiful as a goddess," he told Hephaestus.

"Careful," said Hephaestus, chuckling. "If her beauty rivals Hera's or Athena's or Aphrodite's, the goddesses will give you not a moment's peace!"

"Good point," said Zeus. "Then make her very beautiful, but not beautiful enough to provoke envy on Mount Olympus. And after you have completed the woman, I want you to construct an ornate chest out of precious metals, to fill with gifts."

Hephaestus created a lovely woman who would certainly be irresistible to man. Each of the gods and goddesses contributed to Zeus' project by giving this woman some desirable quality: wisdom from Athena, music from Apollo, charm from Aphrodite, and all sorts of lavish and elegant possessions. Zeus named this woman Pandora, meaning "all gifted."

Pleased with how his plan was going, Zeus handed Pandora the golden box that Hephaestus had constructed. Zeus warned her never to open it. Then he gave her one last gift: insatiable curiosity.

Zeus presented Pandora and all her treasures to Prometheus' brother, Epimetheus. "The gods have created Pandora to be your wife and a companion to the humans," said Zeus.

But Epimetheus was skeptical. His brother had warned him never to accept gifts from Zeus. "My brother betrayed you by stealing fire," said Epimetheus, "and even now he is being tortured at your decree. Why, then, are you presenting me with this glorious gift?"

"My gripe is with your brother, not with you," Zeus replied. "I do not wish to turn my back entirely on the humans, so I have created Pandora. I give her to you since you administer to the humans in Prometheus' absence."

Zeus' words convinced Epimetheus, and so Pandora became his wife.

Their marriage was happy, but Pandora could not stop thinking about the box that she was forbidden to open. She really had no choice—Zeus, unwilling or unable to confront the threat of humans directly, had sent a woman to do his bidding. With his gift of curiosity, he had guaranteed that she would become obsessed with the contents of that mysterious box. She would find herself holding it during the day and dreaming of it at night. Finally she could stand it no longer. Cautiously, she broke the seal. Slowly, she lifted the lid. Suddenly, the box flew open and, with a horrible wail, all the terrors of the world flew out—disease and sorrow, gloom and pain, hunger, hatred, dread, and more.

Pandora quickly slammed the lid shut. It was too late! All the evils had managed to escape into the world except for one thing: foreboding. If it had been set free, humans would have had a true sense of life's inevitable misery. The burden would have been too great and they would have perished long ago. So although she unleashed a world of evil, by slamming the lid shut before foreboding could get away, Pandora foiled Zeus' foul plan and preserved hope for humankind. Men and women would endure and flourish, strengthened rather than destroyed by his plot.

SISYPHUS *Greek*

Sisyphus, a wealthy mortal, was cunning—perhaps too cunning for his own good. He thought he could defy Zeus and cheat death, but he was terribly mistaken.

Zeus, the king of the gods, was known for his many affairs with both mortal women and goddesses. But even though his habits were well known, he tried to keep these affairs a secret. One day he took quite a fancy to Aegina, the daughter of the river god, Asopus. He came down to earth and carried her off through the Greek town of Corinth.

Asopus, finding his daughter gone, asked everyone whether they knew what had become of her. Fearing the wrath of Zeus, no one admitted having seen her. No one, that is, except Sisyphus.

"Great river god," said Sisyphus, "I know the fate of fair Aegina. It was Zeus himself who came and swept her away."

"Zeus, eh?" snarled Asopus. "I will have a talk with him."

Asopus approached Zeus and demanded that his daughter be released. Zeus reluctantly released Aegina, but only after Asopus had told him that it was Sisyphus who had informed him about the abduction. Zeus was furious at being betrayed by a mortal. He swore that Sisyphus would pay with his life.

Zeus paid a visit to his brother Hades, the god of the underworld. "I want you to send one of your agents to collect Sisyphus and bring him to your realm of the dead."

"Whatever you say, brother," agreed Hades, who dispatched Thanatos, the god of death, to Sisyphus' house.

When Thanatos arrived, the clever Sisyphus invited him into his home and entertained him.

"You have come a long way," said Sisyphus and smiled. "I bet you are never welcome anywhere. So rest awhile and let me be your host."

Thanatos, disarmed by this friendly display, decided he would enjoy spending a little time in Sisyphus' company.

"Here, let me show you some magic tricks I have been working on," said Sisyphus, and he made doves appear and eggs disappear. Thanatos was very amused and became quite relaxed. "Now let me show you this trick I just invented," said Sisyphus to his guest. He handed Thanatos a pair of handcuffs and invited him to try them on.

Thanatos put the cuffs on—and of course, once bound by the cuffs, he couldn't take Sisyphus back to the underworld with him. When Thanatos did not return to the underworld, Hades dispatched another god to see what had happened to Thanatos and to take Sisyphus from the world of the living. This god succeeded.

But Sisyphus outsmarted Hades again. Before he was brought to the underworld, he told his wife not to bury his body and not to perform any of the ceremonies designed to aid passage into the underworld. When Sisyphus arrived in the underworld, he told Hades that his wife had dishonored him by not performing a proper burial.

"All mortals are entitled to receive a proper burial," Sisyphus exclaimed, and Hades was forced to agree with him.

"You have three days to straighten out your affairs. But then you have to come right back to me," said Hades.

The three days came and went, but Sisyphus didn't return to Hades. Zeus had caught wind of Sisyphus' ongoing impiety and his anger seethed. He instructed Hades to send guards to collect Sisyphus' soul and to perform all the necessary burial ceremonies. But then Zeus decided that death was not adequate revenge against this conniving mortal. Instead Zeus wanted the fate of Sisyphus to become an example for all mortals who dared defy the gods.

Upon Sisyphus' return to the underworld, Zeus condemned him forever to roll a huge boulder up a very steep mountain, only to have it roll back down again when he was just about to reach the top. Then Sisyphus must begin his labor again. Sisyphus still struggles and strains in this futile effort, every minute of every day.

ICARUS *Greek*

The Athenian inventor and craftsman, Daedalus, was a genius. His greatest challenge was to build an endless, inescapable maze to house a monster known as the Minotaur, a flesh-eating creature that was half man, half bull.

The Minotaur was the offspring of the wife of King Minos of Crete and a prize bull. King Minos was supposed to have sacrificed the bull to the god Poseidon, but at the last minute he changed his mind. Furious, Poseidon made King Minos' wife fall in love with the animal. The result of that union was the Minotaur.

Minos' wife wouldn't allow the king to kill the monster, so instead he had Daedalus build a labyrinth from which the Minotaur couldn't escape. Minos, who was not a kind man, benefited from this arrangement: He placed his enemies within the maze, where it was only a matter of time until the Minotaur found and devoured them.

One of the people condemned to the labyrinth was a hero named Theseus. But he had the foresight to seduce King Minos' daughter, Ariadne, and from her he learned how to escape from the maze. With this knowledge, he killed the Minotaur and fled with his life and the king's daughter.

Furious, King Minos blamed Daedalus for Theseus' escape. The king imprisoned Daedalus and his young son and apprentice, Icarus, in a tall tower to live out the rest of their days. Almost immediately, Daedalus began planning an escape. He and Icarus stared out the tower window. While Daedalus weighed possibilities, Icarus idly watched the birds soar around the tower and roost in the cracks between the stones.

"If we leave by land," the inventor said to his son, "the king's soldiers will find us. And if we leave by sea, we will be spied by the king's ships."

Icarus, who wasn't really paying much attention to his father, said dreamily, "I wish we could just fly out of here."

The fanciful thought rang a bell in Daedalus' head. "Perhaps we *can* fly out!" he said as he began to make some sketches on the dusty floor with his fingertip.

Over the next few months, Daedalus and Icarus collected many feathers from birds they managed to lure into the tower. They gathered bits of wax from a beehive they were fortunate to find outside their window. Daedalus managed to carve some sticks out of some of their furniture. Then he stitched and stuck together all these things to produce two enormous sets of wings.

"This is our chance to fly to freedom," he told Icarus as he strapped the wings on the boy. "You have been studying the birds so you know how they move. Mimic their movements with these wings of your own, Icarus."

"Yes, Father," said Icarus distractedly. He couldn't wait to try out the new wings.

"But remember, son," Daedalus added, "do not fly too near the water, for the dampness will weigh your wings down. And do not fly too high, because the sun will melt the wax that binds your wings together."

"Yes, Father," said Icarus, whose mind was already soaring among the clouds.

Now the pair were ready. Daedalus, perched on the window sill, was the first to leap out of the tower and test the wings. When he was certain they were safe, he called for Icarus to follow. Out Icarus flew, and off he and his father went, sailing through the air with his father's invention.

It wasn't long before Icarus grew eager to test the capabilities of his new wings. Completely forgetting his father's words, he began swooping and soaring to see how high he could fly. As he caught an updraft, the boy climbed higher and higher, losing himself entirely in his newfound freedom. But then the heat of the sun began to melt the wax that held his feathers in place. They began to droop and fall off, slowly at first, then faster. Only then did the doomed boy recall his father's warning. It was too late. Flipping end over end, he plunged into the sea.

Daedalus turned to check on the boy's progress but couldn't see him anywhere.

"Icarus! Icarus! Where are you?" he shouted. There was no response. Then the distraught father looked down and saw the debris of feathers and sticks floating in the water below. The gods had put Icarus in his place.

Osiris Is Murdered by His Brother
Egyptian

Maybe it was because Osiris was tall and handsome. Maybe it was because he ruled over all of Egypt. Or maybe it was because Set's wife seduced Osiris and bore his child. For whatever reason, Set loathed his brother.

Osiris, the stately god of vegetation, had civilized the Egyptian people, showing them how to grow crops and teaching them that cannibalism wasn't such a good idea. From the very beginning, Set resented his brother's popularity, and when Osiris went off to spread civilization throughout the world, Set plotted to steal the throne from him. But unfortunately for Set, Osiris' wife, Isis, kept things in order and foiled his plans.

Set realized that if he ever wanted to rule Egypt, first he would have to kill Osiris. Once when Osiris was sleeping, he secretly measured him very carefully. Then he commissioned a spectacular box of rare woods and precious metals to be made to Osiris' exact dimensions. He enticed seventy-two conspirators to join him in his plan by offering them positions in his new government. They were to play the parts of guests at a party Set was throwing in Osiris' honor.

At the party, Set wheeled out the ornate box he had built. "This magnificent chest will belong to whoever fits in it perfectly," he declared.

One by one everybody at the party lay in the box, but it suited none of them. Finally it was Osiris' turn. He lay in the box—a perfect fit. All at once Set slammed down the lid and the conspirators nailed it shut and sealed it with hot lead so that Osiris would suffocate. Then they heaved the chest into the Nile, where it floated out of sight.

When Isis found out what happened to her husband, she was

stricken with grief. She donned mourning clothes, but she knew her husband would not be able to rest until the proper burial ceremonies were performed, and for that she needed to find his body.

Isis wandered everywhere, asking everyone if they had seen the ornate chest. Some children told her they had seen it floating down the river. As Isis traveled downriver in search of her husband, she heard talk of a tamarisk bush on the Nile's shore near Byblos that had grown to be an enormous tree almost overnight. She suspected that such magical goings-on must have some connection with her husband, and her powers of divination told her that the chest was within the trunk of the tree. She immediately set off for Byblos. She was tired when she arrived, so she rested by a fountain. As she rested, two royal handmaidens came by to fetch some water. Concealing her identity, she began speaking to them. They were bewitched by her beauty and her fragrance, and they allowed her to braid their hair.

"I have heard stories of a miraculous tamarisk tree that grew to enormous size overnight," began Isis.

"This is no idle story," replied the first handmaiden. "Such a tree exists."

"And where is it?" asked Isis. "I would like to see such a miraculous tree."

"Our king was so impressed with it that he had it fashioned into a pillar in his great hall," answered the second maiden.

The handmaidens then bade Isis farewell and carried their water to the palace. Queen Astarte noticed how lovely the handmaidens smelled and asked them where they had found such a delightful fragrance. They told Astarte of the woman at the fountain. Intrigued, Astarte asked them to find the mysterious woman again and invite her to the palace.

Isis and Astarte got along famously, and the queen hired Isis to be nursemaid to her infant son. Isis nourished the baby by giving him her finger to suck. At night, in secret, she would place the infant among the burning embers of the fireplace in order to make him immortal. Then she would turn herself into a sparrow and fly around the pillar that concealed her husband, chirping mournfully.

One night, just after Isis had placed the baby into the fire, Astarte walked in.

"What have you done to my child?" screamed the queen, racing to the hearth and pulling her child from the flames.

"Kind queen, I love your child as if he were my own. The flames were burning away his mortality. If he had stayed in, he would have lived forever. But now the spell is spoiled."

Astarte noticed that her child came from the fire unscorched and unscathed, so she knew magic was involved.

"Who are you?" she asked. "Why have you come here?"

"I am Isis. I have come to reclaim the body of my husband, Osiris, whom I believe is entombed within the pillar of your great hall."

Astarte apologized for shouting at the goddess and promised to do everything in her power to help. She explained the situation to the king, who gave her the pillar. Isis cut it open, revealing the ornate chest within. Isis immediately fell upon it, wailing so loud and violently that one of Queen Astarte's children died of fright.

Isis brought the chest back to Egypt. She opened it and looked upon the body of her dead husband and wept. Then, she transformed her arms into bird wings; flapping them before Osiris' body, she created a life-giving breeze, and by uttering incantations she was able to bring Osiris back to life temporarily. They embraced, made love, and were together until death reclaimed him.

From this encounter Isis conceived a son, Horus, who was destined to avenge his father's death and inherit his kingdom. Isis concealed Osiris' gravesite in the desert and went off to a remote island to raise Horus in secret, safe from Set's evil powers.

One night, while hunting in the bright moonlight, Set discovered Osiris' body. This was his last chance to be rid of his brother forever, so he chopped the corpse into fourteen pieces and scattered them throughout Egypt. "Now," he thought, "Osiris cannot return from the dead, and I am the heir to all of Egypt." Meanwhile, Osiris' son Horus was growing up strong and healthy.

When Isis heard of this latest abomination she left Horus with caretakers and sailed up and down the Nile in a papyrus boat, searching for the pieces of her husband.

Many years passed before Isis managed to collect all parts of her husband's body. Horus had by this time grown to manhood. Together, mother and son reassembled Osiris, anointed him with spices and ointments, and wrapped him in fragrant linen. This funereal treatment was the origin of the Egyptian mummification process. Reciting incantations, Isis and Horus brought Osiris back to life again.

Osiris then gave Horus his blessing and passed the rule of Egypt over to his son. In return, Horus promised to exact revenge on Set. Satisfied, Osiris ascended to the world of the gods, where Ra, the sun god, appointed him ruler of the land of the dead.

The day soon came for Horus and Set to meet and settle the score. The battle was lengthy and vicious, the opponents' strength being closely matched. Finally Horus had the advantage and was about to issue the fatal blow, when Isis intervened.

"Horus, release him!" she commanded.

Horus had no choice but to obey his mother, who used her powers to make him comply. He released his archenemy, who ran off.

"Mother, how can you do this?" cried Horus. "You have disgraced all of us by denying justice. Set must be punished."

Horus was so furious with his mother that he tore the crown from her head.

"Horus," his mother explained, "it is the nature of the world that there be evil as well as good, so that people might choose. It is also your job to continue to do battle against Set. In this way, order and balance will be maintained. Only by fighting this perpetual battle can you avenge your father's death."

Horus reluctantly accepted his mother's wisdom, and looked forward to his next battle with Set.

THE PRINCESS OF PURITY *Chinese*

King Miao Chuang and his wife, Pao Te, had three daughters but no sons. They wanted their daughters to marry within their class in order to preserve the integrity of their empire. Their two oldest daughters married important, influential men and made their parents proud. But the youngest daughter, Maio Shan, had other ideas.

"I do not wish to marry, Father," said Maio Shan. "I want to throw off the physical world entirely and seek perfection. My own goal is to join the convent of the White Bird and to reach Buddhahood."

"To disobey me is treason, child," said the king. "Who ever heard of a princess becoming a nun? It is absurd! Until you start making sense, you are no longer a part of this family. Go then to your convent and think it over. You will see that the holy life is easier spoken about than lived."

Maio Shan set off for the convent of the White Bird early the next morning. But the night before, the king had secretly sent a messenger to the head of the convent to assure that his daughter was given the most grueling tasks to perform. Maio Shan was assigned kitchen duty, where she would be responsible for preparing the meals for five hundred nuns.

"This is a test, Miao Shan," said the mother superior. "Though we aim to transcend the physical world, we are still of this earth. If you fail to prepare our meals properly, you will be sent home."

Maio Shan agreed to the terms, and then prayed for success in reaching her spiritual goals. Her prayers reached Yu Huang, the Master of Heaven, who was touched by the woman's devotion. He dispatched a sea dragon to dig a convenient well so that Maio Shan could gather water, a tiger to collect her firewood, birds to harvest vegetables for her, and heavenly spirits to help perform her chores. The enormous meal was prepared in no time.

The mother superior, seeing that Maio Shan was being helped by supernatural means, sent a note to the king: "Though we tried to dissuade your daughter from becoming a nun and even assigned her impossible chores, miracles are occurring that assure her success. If you want Maio Shan to leave the convent, you must remove her yourself."

The king, who was prone to overreact, ordered his army to surround the convent and burn it to the ground, nuns and all. As the soldiers carried out their orders, the five hundred nuns trapped inside prayed for salvation. "This is all my fault," thought Maio Shan. "I have brought about the destruction of this holy place." She prayed to the Master of Heaven to rescue the nuns. Then she took a pin from her hair, pricked the roof of her mouth and spat blood high into the air. Clouds gathered over the convent and rain poured down in torrents, completely extinguishing the fire.

The rain, however, did nothing to quench the king's rage. When his general reported what had happened, the king ordered that his daughter be executed for violating his demands. Maio Shan was taken from the convent and prepared for execution.

The next day, before a large crowd, Maio Shan bravely put her head on the executioner's block. But the executioner's sword broke in two as it touched Maio Shan's neck. He then tried a spear, but it, too, shattered. The king, wanting to be done with this sad affair, ordered that Maio Shan be strangled with a silken ribbon. This finally did the trick. As soon as Maio Shan died, a tiger leapt out of nowhere, dispersing the crowd. It carried Maio Shan's body deep into the forest.

Maio Shan's soul floated away, and when she awoke in her bodiless form, she did not know where she was. Then a guide appeared, dressed in a blue uniform. "I have come to take you to the underworld," he said. "The gods are very impressed with you. You have nothing to fear." Having faith, Maio Shan followed.

The judges of the underworld greeted Maio Shan personally, for her reputation for performing miracles had reached even them.

"We hear that when you pray, you bring goodness," said one of the judges. "We are tired of seeing nothing but evil. Please lift our spirits with a prayer."

"I will," replied Maio Shan, "if you release the prisoners of the hells so that they might enjoy my prayers as well."

Yama, master of the hells, agreed. As soon as Maio Shan began her prayers, light started to fill the underworld. It became brighter and brighter as she continued to pray. Soon the dark regions were as bright as noon. Pain was banished, and the torture instruments were turned to lotus flowers.

"Enough!" snapped Yama, halting everyone's rapture. "You have made a paradise of hell. We appreciate the break in our bleak routine, but the universe must remain a balance of opposing forces like good and evil, pleasure and pain. That is the law of yin and yang. The hells exist as they are because they need to be this way. We appreciate your gift, but we have no use for it here. Therefore, I am sending you back to your body in the upper world."

Suddenly Maio Shan found herself alive again in her own body in the woods. "All my life I have worked to break the bonds of my body," she wept, "and now I find myself trapped in it again."

"Do not despair, my pious one," said a young man who had just come out of the woods. "I am Ju Lai, the Buddha of the West, and I've come to guide you to Hsiang Shan, where you can strengthen your devotion properly."

Maio Shan kneeled in respect and thanked the Buddha. "Where is this place and what will be expected of me?"

"Hsiang Shan is an ancient monastery a great distance from here, on an island inhabited by immortals. There you will reach perfection." Ju Lai told Maio Shan how to get to the island. Then he disappeared. Maio Shan began her difficult journey, but then Yu Huang, master of heaven, took pity on her and sent a tiger to whisk her off to the island.

At Hsiang Shan, Maio Shan's devotion led her to the pinnacle of perfection and enlightenment and she was declared a Buddha after nine years. For just as long, her father, King Maio Chuang, had been suffering miserably from festering, painful sores and boils that were his punishment from Yu Huang for burning the convent of the White Bird and for similar sins. These ulcers covered his body, and no doctor could cure them or ease his misery. In desperation, he proclaimed that whoever could cure his affliction would succeed him on the throne.

Word of the king's malady reached Maio Shan. She disguised herself as a physician-priest and called upon her father.

"I have no need of a priest," complained the king to his disguised daughter.

"I am also a physician from an old family. I have learned some healing secrets that were lost to time."

"Folk remedies!" laughed the father. "You wander the world as a hermit priest and you administer folk remedies. I have had the service of some of the finest doctors, and they could not cure me. How can your old-fashioned potions help?"

"I guarantee that I can cure you," insisted Maio Shan. "Anyway, you have nothing to lose."

"You are right," admitted the king.

The disguised doctor went to work, poking and probing the king, listening to his heart, looking in his ears, and so forth. "I have diagnosed your illness," she said. "It is easily cured, except that the remedy cannot be bought."

"Well, what is it then? Whatever this remedy is, we can have it concocted for us."

"It's not as simple as that," explained the doctor. "Your cure is an ointment made from the hand and eye of a living person. It is the only thing that will work."

"Take him away!" shouted the king to his guards. "This man is no doctor. He is ill himself!"

That night, the king had a dream in which the physician-priest came to him, applied an ointment to his sores, and cured him. The dream was so clear that the king took it as a sign. The next morning he called for the return of the physician-priest.

"I have suffered enough and am ready to take your cure," said the king. "But how do we find someone who will sacrifice an arm and eye?"

"If you send your ministers to the monastery at Hsiang Shan, they will find a holy person there who will give them what they need," replied the physician. "But they must be sure to strictly observe Buddhist rules throughout their journey."

The king dispatched his ministers to Hsiang Shan, and he ordered that the physician be kept under guard until they returned with the remedy. But Maio Shan created a duplicate of the physician, which remained under the guards' watch, while she herself flew back to Hsiang Shan in advance of the ministers' arrival.

Maio Shan greeted the men, who bowed to her respectfully. They presented a letter from the king describing why they had traveled so far.

"Your request will be granted," assured Maio Shan. "Here, take this knife and cut off my left arm and remove my left eye."

The minister couldn't bring himself to do the task. "Hurry!" urged Maio Shan. "You must obey your king. Otherwise your journey will have been for nothing." The unlucky minister did as he was ordered. Blood flowed from the severed arm and smelled sweet as incense. The minister gouged out her eye and put it on a platter next to the severed arm.

"Your task is completed," said Maio Shan stoically. "Go now back to your king. If he should need anything else, I will be here." She then floated into the air and was gone. The ministers paid their utmost respects and offered their gratitude, and then they were off.

The king and queen greeted the ministers and came to inspect the parcel they brought with them. "What great spirit would sacrifice so much for the sake of a foreign king?" wondered the queen. She then burst into tears when she noticed that the severed hand bore a ring that belonged to Maio Shan. "Who else but the king's own daughter!" she sobbed. "She has obtained the state of perfection she had hoped for."

"Nonsense!" scoffed the king. "Her body was lost after her

death. Anyone could have found it and taken her ring."

Maio Shan had by now resumed her place in the body of the physician. The king and queen presented him with the severed arm and eye, and he proceeded to make the healing ointment. He applied the ointment to the king's left side, and the ulcers healed immediately. But on the right side, the balm was ineffective.

"Why is that?" pondered the Queen.

"To heal the right side, we must make the ointment out of the Holy One's right hand and eye. You must send your ministers back to collect these parts."

So the king once again dispatched his emissaries to Hsiang Shan. Once again Maio Shan preceded them and once again she freely gave to the men her right arm and eye and then vanished in a cloud. The stunned ministers returned home, and the physician prepared more ointment, which cured the king's right side instantly and completely.

The king was overjoyed. "You are the only one who was able to cure me," he said to the physician, "and for this I bequeath to you my throne."

"I have no need of worldly things," replied the humble physician. "You were afflicted because of your past misdeeds and cruelty. I have been sent here not only to cure you but also to show you the True Way of Buddhism. I ask only that you rule your people with compassion and leniency." Having said that, the physician-priest floated off to the sky.

The king was greatly moved by the strange healer. His thoughts turned to Miao Shan and how badly he had treated her. "I was a stumbling block on my daughter's road to holiness," he said to the queen. "Now she is gone and I am at fault. Surely this was the cause of my affliction."

"But now you understand the True Way," said the queen, thinking of the ring, so like her daughter's, that had been on the dismembered left hand. "We must go to see the one who gave up her eyes and arms for your sake. She must be thanked personally."

Their pilgrimage was arduous, but eventually the king and

queen arrived at Hsiang Shan. They were led to the most holy place, and there, on a throne, sat Maio Shan, blind and without her arms. Both the king and the queen fell to the ground before her, sobbing and giving thanks for seeing their daughter again. Maio Shan welcomed them and then admitted that she was the priest-physician who had cured him.

Her father, sobbing uncontrollably at his holy but mutilated daughter, said, "I have committed the greatest crime by killing my daughter, and she has sacrificed her eyes and arms for my sake. Never will I forgive myself."

"I have forgiven you your crimes and injustices against me, Father," said Maio Shan. And saying that, Maio Shan's arms and eyes returned to her. She was whole once again.

The king and queen kissed Maio Shan's feet and then journeyed to their kingdom, but only long enough to renounce the throne. Then they returned to their daughter to learn how to live the perfect life.

GLOOSKAP'S LESSONS

Algonquin/Native American

After Glooskap, the trickster god, vanquished his evil brother, Malsum, and created the world, its animals, and its people, he sat back to see how the natural order would unfold. In those days, animals and people all spoke the same language, and they all lived together. Everyone got along, at least at first.

But it wasn't very long before humans began to battle each other, animals competed for space, and treachery and evil began to spread. None of this made Glooskap very happy. He certainly did not want to have to baby-sit the world for all eternity. The world and its inhabitants would have to take care of themselves. They needed to learn how to live in a civilized manner.

"I have set the world in motion," thought Glooskap, "but I am not going to become a slave to my own creation. I have got to get away. But before I do, I will have a gathering and invite every living creature. Then I will let them know they must tend to their own well-being. I will teach them to respect one another and to behave in an ethical fashion, despite their differences."

Word of the gathering spread quickly throughout creation, and everyone showed up, eager for the festivities. They feasted and danced and vastly enjoyed themselves. Then Glooskap made his announcement. "Creatures of earth," he said, "I think you have grown too familiar with each other and are beginning to take advantage of the good things I have provided. Life is easy, yet you covet your neighbor's belongings. You fight for space, yet plenty of space is available. I want you to know that I am very disappointed, though I still love you all. You must solve these problems yourselves, because I am going away."

The animals and people were ashamed of their behavior and saddened that they had driven Glooskap away. They begged and pleaded with their god to stay and teach them the right way to behave.

"You must always act out of respect for one another. You must always be kind to one another. You must work out the details for yourselves," said Glooskap. "But before I leave the world, I will make myself available to you for seven years. Those of you who have dedicated yourselves to making the world a respectful place may benefit from my counsel. To the truly earnest I will also grant any reasonable requests during that time. But before you seek me out, you must first try to solve your problems among yourselves."

Glooskap then cast a spell on all the creatures of the world, causing them to fall entranced into a deep sleep. When they awoke, Glooskap was gone. The world was completely silent. Then everyone began to talk at once. But something strange had happened—everyone was speaking a different language. For the first time, dogs couldn't understand birds; panthers couldn't speak with elephants; and many humans couldn't speak with each other. Glooskap had given every creature a different language. Soon they realized that since they couldn't understand each other, there was no benefit to living together. So the animals and people separated, some going to live in the forests, some on the plains, and some in the oceans.

Time went by, and the new natural order seemed to be working out. Four people remembered Glooskap's promise to advise anyone who could benefit from his wisdom, so they went off to seek his counsel. Traveling far, they reached a land of incredible beauty. In that land they found Glooskap's lovely home.

"What brings you here?" asked Glooskap, ushering them in.

"We have tried to live lives of respectfulness, and now we need your help. We come with wishes that we hope you can fulfill. After all, that is what you promised, is it not?" said the first man.

"If they are worthy, then I will grant them," replied Glooskap. "Tell me what you wish."

"I try to get along with people, but everyone says I am angry and hostile. I try to keep my temper under control, but sometimes I get so impatient," said the first person. "Nobody likes me or wants to do business with me. Not that I really care or anything, because people are basically lousy anyway. But maybe if I were a little less . . . I don't know . . . assertive . . . then I would be able to get along with people better."

"I see your point," said Glooskap. "And how about you?" he said, pointing to the second person.

"Simple," said the second person. "I have dedicated my life to helping others. Whenever I have something, I share it with someone needier than myself. But I've never had much to begin with. I just want to live comfortably, so I can help others without suffering myself."

"And you?" Glooskap asked the third person.

"Well," she said, "I'm poor *and* disliked. People think of me as a beggar, a charity case. I'm not asking for a lot of wealth, just a comfortable life and the respect of my tribe."

"Seems reasonable," said Glooskap. "And how about you?" Glooskap asked the fourth person.

The fourth person was tall and handsome and elegant. To make himself even taller, he stuffed his moccasins with fur, and it was obvious that he spent a great amount of time on his appearance. He stood apart from his three companions and behaved as if they weren't even alive. He was, in a word, conceited.

"As you can see," he began, "I have my looks, my charm, and my stately elegance. But, I'm sure you realize, one can never be too tall or too majestic. That's why I have come to you—to preserve my stature and, if possible, even increase it."

"Hmm," replied Glooskap, "I will see what I can do." He reached into his medicine sack and pulled out four little boxes of ointment, giving one to each person. "Do not open these until you get back to your lodges. Then you can apply the ointment and your wishes will be granted."

The people thanked Glooskap profusely and returned home. On returning home, the hostile man opened his box and found it filled with fragrant oil, which he rubbed on himself, and became patient and caring. The poor man did the same, and found himself surrounded by profitable business ventures. The wretched woman also found fortune, and her generosity with her newfound wealth made her a well-respected woman among her people.

The conceited man couldn't wait until he returned home to see his wish granted. Halfway home he stopped and opened the box, applying the potion to his body. Immediately he felt himself growing taller, which pleased him greatly. But when the growth would not stop, he became alarmed. Then he started sprouting branches and green needles. His lanky legs grew together and were encased in bark. The man's wish was granted, but not quite in the way he expected. He had become a tall, majestic, and beautiful pine tree, the first of its kind.

TARENYAWAGO BECOMES HIAWATHA

Iroquois/Native American

Tarenyawago, the keeper of the heavens, was disturbed by the agonizing cries of the mortals below him. Looking down, he saw fierce giants and cruel monsters stalking the land. He decided he must intercede in order to protect the humans.

Assuming a mortal form, Tarenyawago came down to earth. He destroyed the monsters and giants. Then he went to the people and took the hand of a little girl. "Come, follow us," he said, and he led them to a quiet place where the sun shone and two rivers danced gloriously over huge boulders. Here the people built a longhouse. They lived very happily and their numbers increased. Satisfied, Tarenyawago returned to the heavens.

After many years, when the children had grown and a new generation was beginning, Tarenyawago visited the people. "You must now scatter across the land and become five great nations," he said. From the people he chose a few families. He called these people Tehawroga, "those who speak differently." Immediately, these people began to speak in a new tongue and could no longer understand their former language. Then, taking a little girl by the hand, he guided the Tehawroga to a new place. Tarenyawago gave them tobacco, beans, and corn, and taught them to be hunters and farmers. From these families sprang the Mohawk tribe.

Tarenyawago then returned to the people he had left behind. Again he selected families and, as before, gave these people a new language. Then, taking the hand of a little girl, he led them a great distance to a beautiful wooded place. He called these people Nehawretago, the people of the big trees, and taught them to make tools and weave baskets. They became the Oneida nation and made their home in the tall, green forest.

Three more times, Tarenyawago chose families. Each time he

gave them a new language and chose a little girl to lead them. In this way, the traditions and leadership of the nations were passed from mother to daughter.

In all, Tarenyawago created five great nations—the Mohawk, the Oneida, the Onandaga, the Cayuga, and the Seneca. To each he gave great gifts. In their turn, the Onandagas received spiritual knowledge, the Cayugas received the canoe and navigational skills, and to the Senecas he gave fleet feet and hunting skills.

Some of the people did not share Tarenyago's vision of five great nations. These people headed toward the sunset and built a bridge across the great water known as the Mississippi. But once they crossed, the bridge collapsed and they could never return. They made their lives in the west, never to be seen again by the people of the Five Nations.

Tarenyawago remained in his human form and lived among the Onandaga nation. He named himself Hiawatha. He married an Onandaga woman, and they had a daughter named Minihaha. Hiawatha traveled in a dazzling white birchbark canoe, which sailed on land as easily as it floated on the waters. In this canoe he traveled from nation to nation, advising the tribes and assuring their success.

But one day a savage people came from the northwest. These tribes were warlike and violent, and threatened the Five Nations. Hiawatha called a meeting of the leaders of the Five Nations to discuss what to do about the menace.

By the shore of a lake, the leaders came together. They waited four days for Hiawatha to arrive. At last they saw him, riding in his canoe with his young daughter. Hiawatha greeted each of the leaders, speaking to each in his own language.

Suddenly, a deep darkness covered the land and a thunderous sound filled the air. The leaders looked up and saw a great mysterious bird, black and huge. It slowly circled in the air, flapping its enormous wings and drawing closer and closer to the earth. The men fled in terror, but Hiawatha and Minihaha bravely stood firm. Hiawatha put his hand on Minihaha's head and said blessings as the mystery bird settled to the ground. Minihaha said good-bye to her father, and the great bird carried her off to heaven. The sky brightened again and Hiawatha sat down on the ground, weeping for three days.

Hiawatha never explained why the mysterious bird took his daughter, but many said it was the price he paid to bring peace to his people. After his mourning had ended, he once again assembled the leaders of the Five Nations and told them they were always to act together. They would negotiate their differences and learn to be a strong league of Five Nations, called the Iroquois. Then Hiawatha stepped into his canoe and sailed up to the heavens, where he once again became Tarenyawago.

6

HEAVEN AND
THE UNDERWORLD

WHAT HAPPENS AFTER WE DIE? Unlike myths of nature or lovers or heroes, myths about the afterlife can't be based on observation. People have long speculated about what lies beyond death. At the heart of all these myths is the nearly universal idea that there is an afterlife in one form or another. The inevitability and finality of death is almost too much for the human mind to comprehend. Throughout the world and throughout the ages, all sorts of stories have emerged to explain the inexplicable. Though death is irreversible, they suggest, it is not necessarily the end.

One common theme in afterlife mythology is the concept of justice. Rewards are granted or punishments exacted after death according to one's behavior in life. Thus, we are presented with choices in life and are responsible, to a great extent, for our own destiny in the afterlife. The moral is obvious: Behave yourself now or suffer the consequences later. This idea survives in present-day religions. Perhaps it helps take the sting out of living with the injustices each of us experiences or witnesses every day.

Most cultures separate the realm of the gods from the realm of the dead. The home of the gods is generally conceived to be in or above the sky. But in many instances, the dead are judged or sent to live under the earth.

In virtually every world culture, the mythology of the afterlife reassures the living and provides the motivation to choose a moral life. As these myths and legends reveal, the path one hopes to take for eternity is determined by the choices one makes during life.

ORPHEUS AND EURYDICE *Greek*

Orpheus, the son of Apollo, was the greatest musician who had ever lived. His instrument was the lyre, and when he played it, trees bowed toward him, wild beasts were tamed, armies put down their weapons, and even the rocks gathered around him.

The love of his life was a fair maiden named Eurydice, whom he wooed and married. But the wedding was cursed by bad omens. The loving couple had been married only a few weeks, when a shepherd spied Eurydice in a field and pursued her. As she fled from him, she stepped on a snake, which bit her pale ankle, and she died.

Orpheus' grief was boundless. To console himself, he played his lyre and sang a song of mourning so sad and compassionate that even the gods were moved to tears. He sang of his beautiful Eurydice and how she brightened everything around her. Now she was doomed to spend eternity in Tartarus, the awful realm of the dead, where beauty and kindness had no place. He sang of opportunities lost, dreams denied, and a world where love brings only pain. In his song, he promised Eurydice that he would pursue her to Tartarus, where the living are not welcome, and he would restore his love to the world of the living. The gods were so touched by Orpheus' song that they granted his wish to go rescue Eurydice from the land of the dead.

So Orpheus began his long journey in search of his wife. The entrance to Tartarus was a dank and winding cavern that snaked deep within the earth. The air was deathly still, but as Orpheus descended he began to hear the wailing of ghosts up ahead. He came to the gate at the entrance to Tartarus, where Cerberus, the three-headed dog, kept guard, his slavering mouth full of knife-sharp fangs. But with the soothing music of his lyre, Orpheus calmed Cerberus, who slept for the very first time.

With his music, Orpheus also persuaded somber Charon, the

ferryman, to carry him across the river Styx into the domain of Hades and Persephone, the king and queen of the dead. Charon's boat groaned under the weight of its living cargo.

Orpheus passed countless ghosts before reaching Hades and Persephone, sitting on their thrones. Through song, he told them of his Eurydice, how he had lost her and had come looking for her. He sang of love—the love that rules the land of the living must surely have power among the dead. He sang of the inevitability and finality of death, but begged for Eurydice to be given more time among the living before she spent eternity among the dead.

His song rang through the dank silence of Tartarus and for a moment reminded the dead of the lost pleasures of life. Here was wily Sisyphus, condemned to roll a huge boulder up a steep hill eternally for disrespecting the gods. The music made him stop and lean against his rock. Equally entranced was Tantalus. For stealing ambrosia from the gods, he had been condemned to be submerged up to his neck in water, yet whenever he grew thirsty and wanted to drink, the water subsided. Above him, always just out of reach, hung boughs of luscious fruit. Thus he was doomed to perpetual hunger, thirst, and anticipation. But now, hearing Orpheus' sweet strains, he felt satiated. Ixion, too, forgot his punishment. For trying to seduce Hera, he was bound to a flaming wheel and flogged. Orpheus' lovely music brought tears to Persephone's eyes, and even Hades' heart softened.

"Orpheus," said Hades, "though many pray for what you ask us, none have ever braved a visit. Your song has moved us. It is true that love is not without power in the land of the dead."

"We will honor your request," added Persephone, "but we must set a condition on it."

"Whatever it is, I will meet it," swore Orpheus, himself in tears.

"Eurydice must follow behind you in total silence, and you may not turn to look at her until you both are back in the land of the sunlight. Obey this and she will be yours for the rest of your natural lives. Disregard it, and Eurydice will remain in the land of the dead forever."

147

Persephone called for Eurydice, who came limping out on her wounded foot.

"Eurydice!" called Orpheus, as he ran to embrace her.

"Do not touch her or talk to her!" warned Persephone. "Leave now in silence."

And so without a word Orpheus led the way and Eurydice followed him over the river Styx, past Cerberus' gate, and finally through the winding and treacherous cave back to the living world. Throughout their long journey Eurydice made not a single sound. Orpheus couldn't even be sure she was really behind him. But Persephone's words rang in his ears and he didn't dare look back.

After a long and arduous climb, Orpheus began to see a glimmer of light up ahead. It grew brighter as he grew nearer. He was close to the end of the cave. He walked a little faster as he approached the light. Finally he reached the end of the cave and stood in the bright sunshine. Impatiently, he turned toward the cave to look at last upon his wife. But it was too soon! Eurydice was still within the cavern's walls. As she was whisked back to Tartarus, she had time to say but one word: "Farewell!"

He began to pursue her, but he knew it was futile. Eurydice was lost to him.

Aeneas Faces His Future *Greek/Roman*

Aeneas, a prince of Troy, saw his city destroyed in a fiery battle against the Greeks. Escaping the inferno, he carried his elderly father on his back. After a time, he encountered other refugees from the city who wanted Aeneas to lead them to a new home where they could settle. They boarded ships and sailed to places unknown, encountering many strange situations—some pleasant, others dangerous. En route to the new settlement, Aeneas' father, Anchises, died. Aeneas felt a great loss.

Eventually, Aeneas and his people arrived in Carthage, which was ruled by Princess Dido. She welcomed the refugees and in time fell in love with Aeneas. He returned her affection, and Aeneas' people began to believe that Carthage would be their new home. But after a number of months, Aeneas received a message from the gods telling him that he must sail farther.

With great reluctance, Aeneas bade farewell to Dido. She was inconsolable with grief. As Aeneas' ships sailed, she ordered her slaves to build a funeral pyre upon which she threw herself. Now a distance off, Aeneas noticed the smoke from the pyre but was ignorant of its cause.

At last the ship arrived on the coast of Italy. Aeneas sought the cave of a seer called the Sibyl.

"I dreamed," said Aeneas to the Sibyl, "that I must visit my father in the underworld so that he can tell me my future. Can you assist me in this mission?"

"The journey to the land of the dead is not easy for anyone, Aeneas," said the Sibyl. "Before I can help you, you must prove that you are worthy of the mission. Find for me a tree with golden branches and bring a branch back to me. For in the underworld, Charon will demand it."

Guided by the gods, Aeneas went into the forest, found the

tree without difficulty and removed one of its golden branches. Because he had accomplished this task, the Sibyl agreed to accompany him on his journey to the underworld.

The entrance to the underworld was near Vesuvius, surrounded by plumes of smoke and lava, sulfurous vapors, and deep craters. In this forbidding landscape, Aeneas and the Sibyl entered a dark cave. "Don't lose your courage," warned the Sibyl.

They passed the loathsome figures of Grief, Disease, Age, Fear, Toil, Worry, and others, each more horrible than the last. They passed monsters—many-headed hydras, fire-breathing chimeras. Then they came to a river, black as tar. The banks were crowded with people, and Charon, the ferryman, selected those whom he would take across the waters.

"Only those who have had a proper burial can cross," explained the Sibyl. "Anyone else must wander a hundred years before riding the ferry."

Charon at first refused to take Aeneas and the Sibyl, since they were of living flesh, but when Aeneas showed him the golden branch, he consented. Once across the river they encountered the spirits of dead children, wailing eternally; then the suicides, bemoaning their final action on the earth. Then they passed those who died of unrequited love, their sadness still enduring. Here, Aeneas recognized Dido and called to her.

"Dear Dido, was I the cause of this? I left Carthage reluctantly, following the commands of the gods!"

Dido looked at him momentarily, but then turned away and walked on, her head bowed in perpetual grief.

Next, they came to a fork in the road, one path leading to the Elysian Fields and the other to the entrance to the city of the condemned. From behind the walls of this city came the sound of chains rattling, iron clanking, and boulders scraping. No god or man could escape this hell: a hydra with fifty heads guarded its gates. The Titans resided in this region, chained at the bottom of a deep pit. Sisyphus also toiled here, rolling a massive boulder up to the top of a mountain only to have an unseen force send it back down again. Then he would begin his arduous ascent once more.

Aeneas and the Sibyl turned away from the dismal region of the condemned and came at last to a brighter realm, the Elysian Fields. Here founders of the Trojan state, war heroes, poets, artists, and priests enjoyed eternal bliss. Aeneas looked admiringly upon the inhabitants who joined in games, sports, singing, and dancing. They lingered on the lush, green fields and listened to beautiful music. Then the Sibyl approached a group of revelers to inquire the whereabouts of Aeneas' father, Anchises.

At last, Aeneas met his father, whose vitality was restored to him.

"Aeneas!" said Anchises. "How long I have waited for this visit, and how I worried as I watched your progress through the seas."

"Father," cried Aeneas, "my thoughts of you were my beacon, guiding me away from danger and urging me onward." He tried to embrace his father, but his longing arms closed on empty air.

The two men wept with joy at the sight of each other. Then Anchises told Aeneas what the future had in store for him.

"Make your home in Italy, where you have landed. Here you will found a powerful new empire—the largest the world has ever seen. Many will be your children and great will be your name. Your people will be mighty in battle and accomplished in the arts. Your empire will be called Rome and long will it thrive."

Grateful for the news and even more happy to have seen his father, Aeneas said a reluctant farewell, and the Sibyl escorted him safely back to the world of the living.

DEATH WITH HONOR *Norse*

The Norse gods were not immortal. Almost from the beginning, Odin, the chief god, knew that the gods were destined to be destroyed by their enemies, the frost giants. Even so, he clung to the hope that he could change his fate if only he could assemble a large and powerful army against the giants and monsters.

To seek out the bravest of the brave, Odin enlisted the help of the Valkyries, supernatural women warriors who rode magnificent flying steeds or donned swans' wings. Though astoundingly beautiful, the Valkyries were invisible to all but those about to die. They flew over battlefields and noted which men fought bravely and died heroically. They also had the power to choose who lived, who perished, and to which side victory would fall. Then they reported back to Odin, who invited the fallen heroes to join him in Valhalla, his magnificent hall for the slain.

Valhalla gleamed with gold and silver. Its beams were made of spears. Its roof was shingled with shields. Its walls held five hundred and forty portals, each wide enough to allow eight hundred armored soldiers to pass through.

For sport, the warriors in Valhalla fought battles to the death against each other every morning. By evening they would rise again and enjoy huge banquets where the mead and beer flowed freely, poured by the beautiful Valkyries from ornate drinking horns. Though Odin enjoyed the beverages, his portion of meat went to his wolves, Geri and Freki, which lay at his feet. In this manner the heroes trained and waited for Ragnarok, the ultimate battle with the frost giants.

The afterlife for the rest of humanity was not so grandiose. Hel was the name of the realm of the dead and also of its ruler. Hel was the daughter of Loki, the trickster giant who caused the gods so much trouble. One half of her face was beautiful; the other half was rotted, like a corpse. When she was born, Odin threw her into Niflheim, the region below Midgard, and here she established herself among the dead. In her halls, hunger was the table, starvation the knife. Anguish formed her wall hangings, and her bed was the sickbed. Her servants were Delay and Waiting.

Though Hel had untold miseries at her disposal, her dominion wasn't necessarily a place of total dread. It was home to all the dead, or to anyone who didn't die heroically on the battlefield. In many ways, one's death in Hel was a mirror of one's life. The realm wasn't reserved for humans alone. In fact, Baldur, the most beloved of the gods, became one of its most famous and tragic residents.

In Asgard, Baldur was plagued with terrible dreams of his own death. He told his troubles to his mother, Frigga, who became quite distressed upon hearing them.

"An ill omen indeed," said Frigga, shaking her head. "Such dark visions are not to be ignored. We must find a way to protect you."

She at once set off to exact an oath from everything on earth that they would not hurt Baldur. Fire and water swore to do no harm to Baldur. Iron and other metals promised to pose no threat. Trees, animals, insects, stones, sticks, poisons, and diseases all swore to leave Baldur unscathed and unsullied. Though exacting, Frigga's mission was not difficult because all of creation loved Baldur, who radiated beauty and innocence.

Now that Baldur was invulnerable, the other gods amused themselves by hurling rocks and hammers and swords and arrows at him. Every projectile would bounce off the god; each weapon was deflected harmlessly by his body. The gods were delighted with this new sport. All, that is, except for Loki.

Loki, who befriended and tormented the gods, seethed with jealousy over the adoration and attention paid to Baldur. He disguised himself as an old woman and paid a visit to Frigga's mansion.

"I see the gods pit themselves against one of their own," said the disguised Loki. "Pray tell me, what has the sole god done to invoke such wrath?"

"What you see, old woman, is not as it appears," explained

Frigga. "The god they so beset is Baldur. Nothing can harm him, so the gods entertain themselves by testing his resilience."

"Nothing can harm him at all?" exclaimed Loki. "But how can that be?"

"I have exacted an oath from all things on earth. All swear to do Baldur no harm," replied Frigga.

"Every animal?" asked the incredulous Loki in his disguise.

"From the smallest germ to the greatest elephant," said Frigga, nodding her head.

"Every mineral and every element?"

"Each one, and water and fire as well," responded Frigga.

"Every plant, from tiny spore to mighty cedar?"

"I have exacted an oath from all plants but one," Frigga revealed. "The plant called mistletoe that grows on the east side of Valhalla. It was too young and frail to be responsible for such an oath."

"I see," said Loki, who was already formulating a dastardly plot. He bade Frigga good day and went on his way.

Loki wasted no time getting to the east of Valhalla to clip a sprig of mistletoe. He then raced to where the gods were playing with Baldur. Hodur, Baldur's blind brother, sat apart from the rest of the gods.

"Why not join the fun?" asked Loki.

"My blindness prevents my participation," replied Hodur. "Besides, I have nothing to lob."

"Nonsense," Loki goaded him, "I'll hear none of that. Here. Take this twig and toss it at the god. I'll guide your aim and make it true."

Loki handed the sprig of mistletoe to Hodur, who threw it as hard as he could at Baldur. The sprig flew through the air and pierced Baldur's heart, killing him.

Baldur died. First there was stunned silence from the gods, then loud lamentations. In the confusion, Loki slipped away.

For their fallen brother the gods prepared a funeral of the highest honor. They placed Baldur's body on his favorite boat, set it afire, and cast it adrift.

Inconsolable in her grief, Frigga determined to retrieve her son from the realm of the dead. Odin's son Hermod volunteered to ride to Hel and negotiate Baldur's release. For this mission, Odin loaned Hermod the use of his eight-legged horse, Sleipnir.

Even though Sleipnir could outrun the wind, the journey to Hel took a full nine days and nine nights. Sleipnir carried Hermod through valleys and woods of total darkness, negotiated impossible slopes, and traversed bottomless pools. Finally, Hermod reached the river Gyoll, the boundary of the realm of the dead. The bridge across Gyoll was paved with gold. On the far side, the maiden of the bridge asked him who he was.

"Yesterday, five hundred men crossed over this bridge," said the maiden, "and not one of them made as much clatter as you. You haven't the look of the dead. Why are you here?"

"I come to seek Baldur. Has he passed this way?"

"Indeed he has and now he is in the realm of the dead." The maiden then pointed out the path that Baldur had taken. Hermod thanked her and rode off. The path wound its way to the barred gates of Hel, where the ferocious two-headed hound, Garm, kept guard. Hermod dismounted Sleipnir, fastened the saddle more tightly, remounted, and leaped over the gate without so much as brushing it. Even Garm, slavering and barking, was no match for Sleipnir's speed.

Hermod then rode to a large palace and found Baldur in a luxurious dining hall, a great feast set before him. As it was terribly late and Hermod was weary, he spent the night in Baldur's company. The next morning he sought Hel, the ruler of the dead, and argued for the return of Baldur to the world of the living.

"If Baldur is as beloved as you say he is, and if he is so sorely missed among the living," replied Hel, "then you must prove this to me. If every person and object in your world weeps for Baldur, then my hold on him is broken, and he may return to the living. But if one creature or creation fails to shed a tear, then Baldur remains mine."

Hermod mounted Sleipnir and brought the words of Hel back

to Asgard. The gods lost no time dispatching messengers to every corner of the world to beg everything and everyone to weep for Baldur. All things eagerly complied, but as the messengers were returning with the good news, they came upon a bent and ancient hag, a giantess named Thokk, who lived in a cave.

"What has Baldur ever done for me?" spat the hag. "Whether he lives or dies is no concern of mine, just as whether I live or die is of no concern to him. Let Hel keep what is hers. Shed a tear? I think not!"

No amount of persuasion could make the hag change her mind.

Defeated, the messengers crossed the rainbow bridge back to Asgard. Even from a distance, the gods knew that they had failed. They also knew beyond any doubt that the hag with the hard heart was actually Loki in disguise.

Sayadio in the Land of the Spirits
Iroquois/Native American

Sayadio was a young Iroquois brave who cared deeply for his younger sister. As children they would invent games and languages that only they could understand. The two were inseparable, and as they grew older, Sayadio protected and defended his sister. But one day, she became ill and no medicine would cure her. In a week she was dead.

Holding his sister's hand as she drew her final breath, Sayadio swore, "I will not leave your side. I will find you in the Land of the Spirits and bring you back to the living world."

Torn by grief, the disconsolate brother traveled years in his search for an entrance to the Land of the Spirits, but no one could tell him how living flesh could enter that realm. Then, on the verge of giving up his quest, he met an old mystic who gave him the secret to making the passage. Sayadio thanked him profusely and was turning to leave when the old man stopped him.

"One more thing, Sayadio," he said, handing him a hollow gourd. "Take this with you. You will find it invaluable."

The young man took the gift and opened it. "But it's empty!"

"No. It is filled with magic. When you find your sister, put her soul in the gourd. There it will be safe for its journey back to this living world."

Sayadio thanked the stranger again and began his trek to reclaim his sister's soul. Eventually, he reached his goal and entered the Land of the Spirits. Much to his surprise, instead of greeting him, the spirits fled from him in horror. Dejected and depressed over the idea that he had made the trip to no avail, Sayadio sat and pondered what to do next.

Then he noticed the spirit of Tarenyawago, who had lived on the earth as Hiawatha, the founder of the confederacy of Iroquois nations. In the Land of the Spirits he presided over all spiritual ceremonies. Sayadio mustered his nerve to approach Tarenyawago and was relieved to be received with courtesy.

"Great Tarenyawago," said Sayadio, "I have come very far to collect the spirit of my sister, whom I feel has been taken unrightfully from the living world."

"You have come at the right time, Sayadio," Tarenyawago explained. "We are just now beginning a dance festival and your sister's spirit will be among the participants. Wait here and you will see her shortly."

Sure enough, the festival started and the spirits gathered for the dance. Sayadio recognized his sister's spirit and ran to embrace her. But as his arms closed around her, she dispersed like fog.

At a loss, Sayadio appealed to Tarenyawago once again.

"Here is a magic rattle," said the kind chief of ceremonies. "Its sound will lure your sister to you."

His hope renewed, Sayadio took the rattle and approached the dancers. As he shook the instrument, his sister's spirit stopped its dancing and began to draw nearer to him. She was transfixed by the rushing sound of the rattle. Soon she drew near enough, and Sayadio, with one swift gesture, whisked his sister's spirit into the hollow gourd and closed the top securely.

Sayadio then returned to his village. His whole tribe gathered around him to witness the ceremony that would reunite his sister's spirit with her body. But just before the ceremony was to begin, a curious young girl opened the gourd to see what treasures it might hold. The sister's spirit flew out and vanished forever.

7

THE END AND
NEW BEGINNINGS

NOTHING LASTS FOREVER. It's a lesson each of us learns at a young age. Just as the wondrous creation of the universe is mirrored in every blossom and baby, the destruction of the universe is implied with every fading flower or the death of a loved one. The flip side of creation is destruction, but in most cultures, the ultimate destruction of the universe is unimaginable. In myths of the universe's end, something lives on, just as many cultures believe that the human soul or spirit lives on after physical death.

The universe will eventually end, but in that ending will be the seeds of a new beginning, a fresh start. Generally, the apocalypse, or cosmic cataclysm, is seen in myth as a battle between good and evil that occurs when their delicate balance is disturbed. The result will be a new universal order, or a kind of cosmic housecleaning. In some cultures, this cataclysm is a onetime event that has yet to happen. Many civilizations have flood myths, in which the gods produce a flood and wipe away the human race (and virtually everything else) in order to start over again. Other cultures foresee the end of the world as part of an ongoing cycle of creation and destruction that always was and always will be.

These myths mirror the human conviction throughout many cultures that in each end there is a new beginning. They provide a means to accept our finality and offer hope for what is to come.

ATLANTIS *Greek*

Long, long ago, the gods of Mount Olympus divvied up the world. Poseidon, the god of the sea, took as his share an island continent situated in the ocean beyond the Straits of Gibraltar, which the ancients called the Pillars of Hercules.

On this island lived a mortal woman named Cleitis. Poseidon fell in love with Cleitis and married her. In the very center of the island, on a tall mountain, Poseidon built a magnificent palace for his bride, along with a shrine and a temple. He then reshaped the island into an earthly paradise. Around the mountain palace he formed two wide, concentric rings of fertile land separated by three equally wide rings of water. Beyond the outermost ring of water lay a sprawling, beautiful metropolis. Throughout the island Poseidon provided ample hot and cold springs, abundant and varied trees, lush pastures, and healthy livestock. Beneath the dark, fragrant earth lay gleaming metals, plentiful and precious. The people of the island enjoyed their bounty and shared their good fortune through brisk trade with the rest of the world.

Cleitis and Poseidon had five pairs of sons. The firstborn was Atlas, and he was declared king of the island, which Poseidon then named Atlantis, after his son. Each of Atlas' brothers was granted a portion of Atlantis as his domain. They vowed that they would never fight against one another and would come to the aid of any brother under attack. Their differences were to be decided through negotiation, but Atlas had the ultimate authority if the brothers could not resolve a dispute.

Quarrying the abundant red, black, and white stones of Atlantis, the people built a beautiful city that shone in the sun. Around the inner land ring they built a tin-clad wall. The outside wall was overlaid with brass, and the wall surrounding the center portion of the island was covered with orichalcum, a metal more rare and costly than gold, but which was abundant on Atlantis.

In this idyllic place the descendants of Poseidon and Cleitis prospered and were happy. Every man and woman worked for the common good, and personal wealth was shunned because every need was met. And so it went for generation after generation.

Eventually, however, as the blood of the gods was diluted over time, human nature got the better of the people of Atlantis. The first stirrings of greed began to infect the population. People began to covet each other's possessions and cheat one another. The hunger for power led them to mount an army to conquer other lands and forge a mighty Atlantean empire. Their army of twelve hundred ships and ten thousand chariots conquered Libya and much of Europe.

Both Italy and Egypt braced themselves for the coming invasion, knowing that they could not rebuff the onslaught. Athens, realizing that it, too, was in the path of the army of Atlantis, joined with the Greeks to defeat the marauders. No other nation dared join the alliance.

The Athenians and Greeks met the enemy at the border of Egypt. The battle was long and difficult, but at last the Atlanteans were defeated. The Greeks then freed the prisoners of war who were enslaved in Atlantis.

That same day, as the Greek troops were sailing back home, a violent earthquake split Atlantis and a tremendous tidal wave submerged the island. The once-glorious continent disappeared into the ocean. Thus, Poseidon punished the greedy and ambitious people of Atlantis for spoiling his vision of a paradise on earth.

TWILIGHT OF THE GODS *Norse*

To build the universe, the gods of Asgard defeated Ymir, the frost giant. But their victory was incomplete because Ymir's descendants, a race of giants, survived.

Led by Odin, the gods banished the giants to Jotunheim and maintained a constant vigil over them. But in the end, these giants would escape and mark the beginning of the end for the gods, who were destined to be destroyed.

The gods knew this, but they could not prevent it. Omens would portend their downfall. Two wolves would devour the sun and moon, and the Twilight of the Gods, Ragnarok, would begin.

First would come three winters, unrelenting, unbearable, uninterrupted by summers. The earth would be engulfed in warfare as monsters slipped their bonds.

In Ragnarok, the giants would overpower the guard of Bifrost, the rainbow bridge to Asgard, the home of the gods. Surt, the fire giant, would lead the way, his flaming sword setting the earth ablaze. Hel, the grotesque guardian of the dead, would cross the bridge next, her rotting minions trailing behind her. Other giants, too—innumerable, unstoppable—would march across Bifrost until the bridge shattered. The shrieks of the giants, the clamor of their feet, the clank of their weapons would rock the earth, causing mountains to crumble and men to die. The tree that upheld and nourished the universe would shudder to its roots, and its leaves would wither and fall. The giants and the gods would converge on Vigrid, the field of the final battle, which stretched one thousand leagues in each direction. Joining in the great carnage would be the children of Loki, monsters horrible beyond imagination and the ultimate enemies of the gods.

Odin, the first of the gods, would be the first fated to die. His sword and golden helmet would prove powerless against the wolf

Fenrir, whose open jaw extended from the lowest valley to the dome of heaven. In vengeance, Vidar, Odin's son, wearing shoes of impenetrable leather, would hold Fenrir's mouth open with his foot and plunge his sword down the wolf's throat.

Thor, god of thunder, would then battle his archenemy, the Midgard serpent, whose arrival would be signaled by a tremendous tidal wave plowing through the ocean. Although Thor's mighty hammer would deal the beast a skull-crushing blow, the monster's dying gasp would spew poison on the god, who would stagger nine steps before dying.

The carnage would continue. Tyr, the bravest warrior of the gods, would be mauled by Garm, the slavering dog-guard of the underworld. Frey, the god of fertility, would die by his own invincible sword, which would fall into the hands of Surt. Eventually, all the gods and all their enemies would perish. With no gods to maintain the celestial order, the stars would flicker out and fall from the sky. All life on earth would dwindle away, leaving only cold rock and stagnant ocean.

And then, somehow, life would begin again. Out from under the bark of the tree that holds the cosmos together a man and a woman, the sole survivors of Ragnarok, would emerge, nourished by nothing more than morning dew. Lif and Lifthrasir would then repopulate the world. New gods, too, would rule the heavens. These gods had always existed but had been lying low, knowing that their day would come. These most ancient yet newest of gods would reseed the land, restock the oceans, and restore the animals. The world would live again.

UTNAPISHTIM AND THE FLOOD *Babylonian*

A time came, not long after creation, when people covered the earth. Their clamor and commotion displeased the gods.

One day the clamor could no longer be overlooked. "Look at them all!" said Enlil to the other gods. "They teem like ants. They bicker and fight. Just listen to the noise and fuss they make. Whose idea was it to make people in the first place? I say let's be done with them."

"I agree with him," said Ishtar. "And what do you think?" she asked the other gods.

All the gods, except for Ea, agreed that humanity was a bad idea and the best course of action was to destroy it and start over again. After the council of the gods adjourned, Ea visited the reed house of Utnapishtim, a deeply devout and well-respected man. Utnapishtim wasn't home, so Ea whispered to the walls of the house: "Utnapishtim, tear down your house of reeds, build a ship, and collect your family and a male and female of every creature on earth. The ship shall measure one hundred twenty cubits long and equally wide. Vault its roof and seal it against the storm to come."

Utnapishtim returned to his house. And that evening, a gentle breeze started to blow across the house, causing the reed walls to vibrate. In the vibrations Utnapishtim heard the warning words of Ea. "I will obey these godly words," he thought to himself, "but it will not be easy to explain it to the neighbors."

First thing the next morning, Utnapishtim gathered all his family around him. They believed what he told them about the voice he had heard and eagerly helped him to cut timbers, fasten planking, and pour pitch. In just a week the ship was complete. Then his family loaded in supplies and helped to round up the animals. No sooner had Utnapishtim's family and craftspeople climbed aboard than the rain began.

At the gods' command, daylight turned to darkness and water surged from the bottom of the ocean and crushed the land like a clod of dirt. Lightning flashed and the roar of the thunder shook the heavens. Even the gods were frightened.

"What have we done?" moaned Ishtar. "This is out of control. All we've worked for we're now destroying! Was this a good idea?"

The gods could say—could do—nothing. The situation was out of their hands. Tempests raged for six days and nights. By the seventh day, the rain had stopped, and the world was still and silent but for one lone ship floating aimlessly over its face. For several days the ship wandered, until, in the distance, Utnapishtim saw the very tip of a mountain. There, on the summit of Mount Nisir, the ship grounded.

Utnapishtim and his family waited patiently for six days. On the seventh day he sent out a dove, but it soon returned, having found no place to make a home. He then set loose a swallow, but it, too, returned. Then he sent out a raven, which didn't return. Joyfully, Utnapishtim realized that the raven had found a place to land. The waters were subsiding. He opened the ship and set the animals free. Then he built a fire and made a sacrifice to the gods, which pleased them.

But Enlil was not pleased. He had never regretted his decision to destroy humanity, and he was furious to learn that some people had escaped the flood.

"Ea!" he shouted. "I know you had something to do with sparing humankind, even though it was against my will. What do you have to say for yourself?"

"Not everyone deserved to die in this flood," Ea replied. "The animals certainly caused no harm to anyone. I think the flood was too destructive; it killed everything without discrimination. Once it started, even you could not control it, Enlil. Utnapishtim and his people are good. Sure, they survived the flood, but do you think they did not suffer from it? That is punishment enough."

"It is true that things did not go as we had planned," admitted Enlil. "I promise to make it up to Utnapishtim." He then visited

Utnapishtim and his wife and said to them, "For all you have been through, I grant to you life everlasting. You will never age nor die. I will never grant this gift to any other mortals, just as I will never allow the world to be flooded again. But because you have received this gift from me and are now more godlike than mortal, you must live forever secluded from the rest of humanity."

Utnapishtim and his wife thanked Enlil. Then they bade their children farewell and went off to live by the mouth of a river, where they reside even to this day.

THE GREAT SERPENT *Fon/African*

All of creation was shaped by Mawu and her twin brother, Lisa. Mawu was the moon—all that is gentle, joyful, forgiving, wise, and nurturing. Lisa was the sun, with a fiery, fierce, strong, and cruel disposition. In the early times, Mawu and Lisa came together, creating an eclipse, and from this union seven pairs of gods were formed, who were to rule over storms, animals, tools, agriculture, and other important matters. Though Mawu and Lisa were separate beings, they were actually two halves of the force that kept the universe in balance. Hence, they were called by the single name Mawu-Lisa. Mawu-Lisa and the other gods shaped the world using the materials provided for them by their creator, Nana Buluku.

Before Mawu-Lisa was created, Nana Buluku assembled the raw materials for the universe inside a giant gourd. Mawu-Lisa then formed the earth, which floated on water in this gourd, and Nana Buluku rode around his creation in the mouth of a giant snake called Da Aido Hwedo. The trail of the snake formed the mountains and valleys and rivers. Da Aido Hwedo's excrement became the precious metal that could be found in the earth.

As Mawu-Lisa created more and more objects to fill the earth, it became obvious that the world was becoming much heavier than they had expected.

"Nana Buluku," said Mawu-Lisa, "we have created a glorious earth, but we fear it is no longer stable and will sink into the ocean. What can be done about it?"

"You should have thought of that before," scolded Nana Buluku. "But I'll tell you what. I like what you have done, so I'll give you Da Aido Hwedo. His coils will support the world, at least for a while, so you may enjoy it and rule over it. But he cannot hold the world forever."

"We are grateful for your generosity," said Mawu-Lisa.

Mawu-Lisa rode Da Aido Hwedo deep into the depths of the ocean. The great serpent then coiled itself, creating a giant spring beneath the earth. But the sea was only large enough to contain half of the serpent. The other half came out of the sea and coiled around the top of the earth, keeping the planet centered within the giant gourd. Part of Da Aido Hwedo formed the rainbow.

The serpent then dipped its head back into the sea and gripped its own tail in its mouth. Mawu-Lisa then created a race of monkeys to live at the bottom of the sea with Da Aido Hwedo. Their task was to feed the serpent iron to maintain its strength.

This was the way Mawu-Lisa supported their creation, but, as Nana Buluku had warned, the solution would not be permanent. Frequently twisting and shifting his position to stay comfortable, Da Aido Hwedo caused many earthquakes. Eventually the monkeys would run out of iron, and Da Aido Hwedo would be forced to devour himself. When that happened, the earth would sink into the sea forever.

QUETZALCOATL *Toltec/Aztec*

Quetzalcoatl was the friend and giver of life of the Toltec people of Mexico. He stole corn from the ants to give the Toltecs food to eat, and he taught them how to mark time by inventing the calendar. He brought the friendly winds to cool them in the hot summer, taught them to make art, and showed them the science of the stars. But even the most benevolent gods have their enemies, and Quetzalcoatl's was the trickster Tezcatlipoca. He wanted people to practice human sacrifice, which great Quetzalcoatl forbade. Like Quetzalcoatl, Tezcatlipoca gave gifts to the Toltecs, but his gifts usually caused more harm than good.

Tezcatlipoca wanted to be the supreme god, so he devised a way to trick Quetzalcoatl so that he could be rid of him. One day, he brought Quetzalcoatl a gift.

"Here, I have brought you a mirror, so that you may see yourself as the world sees you," said Tezcatlipoca.

The benevolent god looked at his reflection and said, "Look at all those lines and wrinkles. I am so old and ugly. Soon people will grow to hate me."

"Don't be silly," replied Tezcatlipoca. "I can fix your face with some makeup." He painted the god's face and body green, red, and yellow. Then he gave him an elaborate mask and adorned him with feathers. "Now look at yourself," Tezcatlipoca said.

"Beautiful!" exclaimed Quetzalcoatl. "And so regal."

Now that Tezcatlipoca had won Quetzalcoatl's trust, the wily trickster made his move. He served Quetzalcoatl and his family an intoxicating beverage until they were too inebriated to know right from wrong. The next morning Quetzalcoatl awoke to find that he had slept with his sister. His shame was immense.

"This sin is unpardonable and unbefitting a god. I must now go away and leave my people," he said.

The people were dismayed to learn that Quetzalcoatl was deserting them. They pleaded with him not to leave, but could not change his mind.

"Do not worry, my friends," said Quetzalcoatl. "I am not abandoning you. One day I shall return to set things right, but for now I must atone for my wrongdoing. Look to the heavens for a sign. It will be my promise that I will come back to you."

Having said good-bye, he began his long trek east. He turned his jungles into deserts, buried all of his wealth, and burned his houses. Then, sailing off on a raft of snakes, he went into exile. Finally, he built a funeral pyre on the raft and threw himself upon it. The sparks from the flame turned into exotic birds, and his heart rose up to become the planet Venus, the sign to his people that one day he would return.

With the god out of the way, Tezcatlipoca was determined to destroy Quetzalcoatl's people. First, he cast a spell on them to make them sing and dance themselves to death. Then, disguised as a puppeteer, he visited the survivors and performed a puppet show, starring a miniature Quetzalcoatl. The show was so entertaining that people trampled each other just to see it. Pretending to atone for the deaths he had caused, Tezcatlipoca urged his audience to stone him, but as the stones hit him, noxious vapors poured from his wounds, killing all who inhaled them.

As a final attack, Tezcatlipoca tainted all the food supply, making it inedible. Then, as the people neared starvation, he appeared as an old woman and began to roast fragrant corn. The aroma drew all the rest of the people from their homes. When they were gathered around the fire, Tezcatlipoca killed them. This was the end of the Toltec people.

Soon, another race, the Aztecs, heard of Tezcatlipoca's treachery and of Quetzalcoatl's defeat. They began to worship the exiled god, believing that one day he would return to defeat Tezcatlipoca and usher in an era of peace and prosperity.

Generations passed as the people watched and waited for Quetzalcoatl's return from across the sea. One day a strange ship was spied on the horizon. As it drew nearer, rumors spread that this must be Quetzalcoatl's return, for the vessel was unlike any the Aztecs had ever seen. Soon the ship reached their land. As the Aztecs gathered eagerly around, out of the ship stepped a godlike figure in the image of Quetzalcoatl.

The Aztecs welcomed their god back to his rightful land, but realized too late that this imposing visitor, who called himself Hernando Cortez, intended to destroy them—just as Tezcatlipoca had destroyed the Toltecs.

GLOSSARY

ΑENEAS (eh-**nee**-us) *Roman* A prince of Troy and the founder of Rome.

ΑMATERASU (**ah**-mah-**tay**-rah-soo) *Japanese* The goddess of the sun.

ΑMEMT (**ah**-memht) *Egyptian* A beast that devours souls deemed impure.

ΑNUBIS (ah-**noo**-bis) *Egyptian* The jackal-headed god who weighs souls in the underworld.

ΑPHRODITE (aff-ro-**die**-tee) *Greek* The goddess of love, born of sea foam. Called Venus by the Romans.

ΑPOLLO (a-**pall**-loh) *Greek* The god of the sun.

ΑPSU (**ap**-soo) *Babylonian* With his wife, Tiamat, the co-creator of the gods.

ΑRTHUR (**ar**-thur) *Celtic* A king of Britain and legendary leader of the knights of the Round Table.

ΑRURU (ah-**roo**-roo) *Babylonian* The mother goddess who creates Enkidu in order to humble Gilgamesh.

ΑSGARD (**as**-gahrd) *Norse* The realm of the gods.

ΑSKE (**as**-kuh) *Norse* The first man, who along with Embla, the first woman, is created by Odin, Vili, and Ve from an ash tree.

ΑTHENA (a-**thee**-nah) *Greek* The goddess of wisdom and warfare. Called Minerva by the Romans.

ΑTLAS (**at**-lus) *Greek* A Titan who is condemned forever to hold the heavens on his shoulders.

ΑTUM-RA (**ay**-tum **ray**) *Egyptian* The first of the gods, whose tears create the human race. Also known as Ra.

ΑUDUMLA (ah-**dum**-lah) *Norse* A giant cow whose milk nourishes Ymir and the race of frost giants.

BEOWULF (**bay**-o-wulf) *Celtic* The brave hero who slays the monster Grendel.

BESTLA (**best**-lah) *Norse* The daughter of the giant, Ymir, and the mother of the first gods.

BIFROST (**bie**-frost) *Norse* The bridge between Midgard (earth) and Asgard (the home of the gods), which appears as a rainbow.

BRAHMA (**brah**-ma) *Hindu* The creator of all things.

BRYNHILD (**brin**-hild) *Norse* Odin's daughter, a Valkyrie who is rescued from a ring of fire by the hero Sigurd.

BUDDHA (**boo**-dah) *Hindu* A person who has attained a state of perfect enlightenment.

BUMBA (**bum**-bah) *Bantu/African* The creator of the sun, moon, stars, animals, and humans.

BUR (**burr**) *Norse* The son of Buri and father of Odin.

BURI (**bur**-ree) *Norse* The first godlike creature, who is born of a block of ice and whose offspring leads to the destruction of the frost giants.

CERBERUS (**sir**-buh-rus) *Greek* The three-headed dog that guards the entrance to Tartarus, the underworld.

CERES (**sear**-eez) *Roman* See Demeter.

CHAOS (**kay**-oss) *Greek* The endless, swirling sea that exists before the earth's creation.

CHARON (**kar**-un) *Greek* The ferryman who carries souls across the river Styx into Tartarus.

COYOTE (ky-**oh**-tee) *Crow/Native American* A trickster who shapes the earth and humans out of mud pulled from the bottom of the endless ocean. Also known as Old Man Coyote.

CRONUS (**krow**-nus) *Greek* The youngest Titan, whose actions set the stage for the birth of the gods.

CUPID (**kyoo**-pid) *Roman* Son of Venus, god of love and desire. Called Eros by the Romans.

CYCLOPES (**sigh**-klops) *Greek* One of the race of one-eyed giants produced from the union of Gaia and Uranus.

DA AIDO HWEDO (**dah eye**-doh **hwee**-doh) *Fon/African* The giant serpent that supports the earth.

DAEDALUS (**deh**-dah-lus) *Greek* A master inventor and the father of Icarus.

DEMETER (de-**mee**-ter) *Greek* The goddess of agriculture and the harvest. Called Ceres by the Romans.

DUAT (**doo**-aht) *Egyptian* A region in the underworld where the ka must pass through to reach the Hall of Judgment.

EA (**ay**-ah) *Babylonian* The all-knowing god, who creates the four winds and kills Apsu.

EDSHU (**ed**-shoo) *Yoruban/African* The god of conflict and confusion.

ELYSIAN FIELDS (eh-**lee**-zhun feelds) *Greek/Roman* Part of the underworld where the blessed dwell after death.

EMBLA (**em**-bla) *Norse* The first woman, who is created by Odin, Vili, and Ve from an elm tree. See Aske.

ENKIDU (**en**-kih-doo) *Babylonian* A man-beast, who matches the hero Gilgamesh in strength and courage.

ENLIL (en-**lil**) *Babylonian* The god of the earth and the air, who sends a flood to destroy all of creation.

EPIMETHEUS (ep-ih-**mee**-thee-us) *Greek* A Titan who helps his brother Prometheus create humans and animals and later marries Pandora.

ERINYES (er-**ih**-nee-us) *Greek* Haglike spirits of vengeance, created from Uranus' blood, who hound and torment murderers. Called the Furies by the Romans.

EROS (**air**-oss) *Greek* The god of love and romantic desire and the son of Aphrodite. Called Cupid by the Romans.

EURYDICE (you-**rih**-dih-see) *Greek* The wife of Orpheus, who dies tragically.

EURYSTHEUS (you-**riss**-thee-us) *Greek* A cowardly king of Mycenae, under whose command Heracles performs his labors.

FAFNIR (**fahf**-nir) *Norse* A ferocious dragon that guards a hoard of enchanted gold and is slain by Sigurd.

FREKI (**freh**-kee) *Norse* A wolf that, along with Geri, lies at Odin's feet in Valhalla.

FREY (**fray**) *Norse* The god of fertility and peace and the husband of Freya.

FREYA (**fray**-ah) *Norse* The goddess of youth and beauty and the wife of Frey.

FRIGGA (**frig**-gah) *Norse* Odin's wife and the mother of Baldur.

FURIES (**fyoo**-reez) *Roman* See Erinyes.

GAIA (**guy**-ah) *Greek* The personification of the earth, who is the mother and wife of Uranus.

GARM (**gahrm**) *Norse* The ferocious two-headed dog that guards the underworld.

GEB (**gehb**) *Egyptian* The god of earth.

GERI (**jeh**-ree) *Norse* A wolf that, along with Freki, lies at Odin's feet in Valhalla.

GILGAMESH (**gil**-ga-mesh) *Babylonian* The heroic son of a goddess and a mortal, and friend of Enkidu.

GLOOSKAP (**gloo**-skap) *Algonquin* A creator and trickster god.

GRENDEL (**gren**-duhl) *Celtic* A monster that terrorizes the king of Denmark and is slain by Beowulf.

GYOLL (**guy**-ahl) *Norse* The river that borders the land of the dead.

HADES (**hay**-deez) *Greek* The god of the underworld. Called Pluto by the Romans.

HECATONCHEIRES (heh-**kah**-tawn-**kee**-air-ays) *Greek* The beast-like children of Gaia and Uranus, who have fifty heads and one hundred hands.

HEL (**hell**) *Norse* The goddess of death.

HEPHAESTUS (heh-**fehs**-tus) *Greek* The craftsman of the gods, who creates the first woman. Called Vulcan by the Romans.

HERA (**hair**-ah) *Greek* The wife of Zeus and the queen of the gods. Called Juno by the Romans.

HERACLES (**hair**-ah-kleez) *Greek* The son of Zeus and one of his mortal mistresses, who is forced by Hera to perform a series of difficult labors. Called Hercules by the Romans.

HERCULES (**her**-kyoo-leez) *Roman* See Heracles.

HERMES (**her**-meez) *Greek* A messenger of Zeus. Called Mercury by the Romans.

HERMOD (**her**-muhd) *Norse* One of Baldur's brothers.

HIAWATHA (hi-ah-**wah**-thah) *Iroquois* See Tarenyawago.

HINE (**high**-nee) *Polynesia* The goddess of death.

HODUR (**hoe**-dur) *Norse* Baldur's blind brother, who is tricked by Loki into killing Baldur.

HORUS (**hore**-us) *Egyptian* The god of light, and the son of Isis and Osiris.

IOLAUS (**eye**-oh-laus) *Greek* Heracles' friend and assistant in performing his labors.

ICARUS (**ih**-ka-rus) *Greek* The son of Daedalus, who plunges to his death when his man-made wings fall apart.

ISHTAR (**ish**-tar) *Babylonian* The goddess of love and war.

ISIS (**eye**-sis) *Egyptian* The principal female god and sister and wife of Osiris, who controls crop growth and fertility.

IZANAGI (ih-zah-**nah**-gee) *Japanese* With his sister, Izanami, co-creator of the earth, heavens, underworld, gods, and humans. Literally, "he-who-invites."

IZANAMI (ih-zah-**nah**-mee) *Japanese* With her brother, Izanagi, co-creator of the earth, heavens, underworld, gods, and humans. Literally, "she-who-invites."

JOTUNHEIM (**joh**-ton-hime) *Norse* The home of the giants.

JUNO (**jyoo**-noh) *Roman* See Hera.

JUPITER (**jyoo**-pih-ter) *Roman* See Zeus.

KINGU (**keen**-goo) *Babylonian* The leader of Tiamat's army in her battle against Marduk, and from whose blood humans are created.

LIF AND LIFTHRASIR (**leef, leefth**-ray-sir) *Norse* The first man and woman after the Twilight of the Gods who will repopulate the earth.

LOKI (**loh**-kee) *Norse* A trickster from a race of giants.

MAAT (**maht**) *Egyptian* The goddess of truth and justice.

MAHUI-IKE (**mah**-oo-ee **eye**-kee) *Polynesian* The keeper of fire and Maui's great-grandmother.

MALSUM (**mahl**-sum) *Algonquin/Native American* The evil brother of Glooskap, and the creator of serpents, mountains, and obstacles.

MARDUK (**mar**-dook) *Babylonian* The creator god who defeats Tiamat, creates the earth and the heavens from her body, and becomes the hero and leader of the gods.

MAUI (**mah**-oo-ee) *Polynesian* The trickster god who separates the sky from the earth and brings fire to humans.

MAWU-LISA (**mah**-woo **lee**-sah) *Fon/African* The creative force represented by Mawu, the moon, and her brother Lisa, the sun.

MERCURY (**mer**-kyoo-ree) *Roman* See Hermes.

MERLIN (**mer**-lin) *Celtic* A magician who helps Uther Pendragon and his son, King Arthur.

MIDGARD (**mid**-gahrd) *Norse* The realm of the earth.

MIDGARD SERPENT (**mid**-gahrd **ser**-pent) *Norse* A venomous monster that encircles the earth.

MINERVA (**mih**-ner-vah) *Roman* See Athena.

MINOS (**mee**-nos) *Greek* A king of Crete who employs Daedalus to build a labyrinth.

MINOTAUR (**min**-oh-tar) *Greek* A monster—half-human, half-bull—that is imprisoned in a labyrinth by King Minos of Crete.

MOUNT OLYMPUS (**mount** oh-**lim**-pus) *Greek* The home of the gods.

MUSPELLHEIM (**muss**-pell-hime) *Norse* The land of fire that lies to the south of Midgard.

NANA-BULUKU (**nah**-nuh buh-**loo**-koo) *Fon/African* The god who assembles the raw materials to form the universe.

NEPHTHYS (**nef**-thiss) *Egyptian* The goddess of dusk and wife of Set.

NEPTUNE (**nep**-toon) *Roman* See Poseidon.

NIFLHEIM (**niff**-il-hime) *Norse* The land of ice and mist where the dead dwell that lies below Midgard (earth).

NUN (**noon**) *Egyptian* The void that exists before creation.

NUT (**noot**) *Egyptian* The goddess of the sky.

ODIN (**oh**-din) *Norse* The chief god, who with his brothers, conquers the frost giants and creates the earth.

ORPHEUS (**or**-fee-us) *Greek* A great musician, and son of Apollo, who tries to reclaim his dead wife, Eurydice, from Tartarus.

OSIRIS (oh-**sigh**-ris) *Egyptian* The principal male god, who brings civilization to Egypt.

PANDORA (pan-**dohr**-ah) *Greek* The first woman, who is created to punish mankind.

PERSEPHONE (per-**sef**-on-ee) *Greek* The daughter of Zeus and Demeter, who is abducted by Hades and becomes his wife and the queen of the dead. Called Proserpine by the Romans.

PLUTO (**plyoo**-toh) *Roman* See Hades.

POSEIDON (puh-**sigh**-duhn) *Greek* The god of the seas. Called Neptune by the Romans.

PROMETHEUS (pro-**mee**-thee-us) *Greek* A Titan who steals fire from the gods for the benefit of humans.

PROSERPINE (pro-**sir**-pine) *Roman* See Persephone.

PSYCHE (**sigh**-kee) *Greek/Roman* A human woman whose beauty rivals that of Venus and with whom Cupid falls in love.

QUETZALCOATL (**ket**-sahl-koh-**ah**-tuhl) *Aztec/Mexican* The creator god who gives humans corn, the calendar, and astronomy.

RAGNAROK (**rag**-nah-rock) *Norse* The ultimate battle between the gods and their enemies, in which the gods are destined to lose. Literally, the "twilight of the gods" or "the destruction of power."

RHEA (**ree**-ah) *Greek* A Titan and the sister and wife of Cronus, whose children become the gods.

SAYADIO (sah-**yah**-dee-oh) *Iroquois/Native American* A young Iroquois man who tries to rescue his sister's soul from death.

SEDNA (**sed**-nah) *Inuit/North American* The spirit of the underworld and of the sea and sea life.

SET (**set**) *Egyptian* The god of darkness, and the brother and enemy of Isis and Osiris.

SHAMASH (sha-**mahsh**) *Babylonian* A protector god.

SHU (**shoo**) *Egyptian* The god of wind.

SIGMUND (**sig**-muhnd) *Norse* A great warrior who passes an invincible magic sword onto his son, Sigurd.

SIGURD (**sig**-erd) *Norse* An epic hero who engages in a series of adventures, which includes rescuing Brynhild.

SISYPHUS (**sih**-suh-fus) *Greek* A mortal who challenges Zeus' power and is condemned forever to roll a huge boulder up a steep hill in the underworld.

SLEIPNIR (**sleep**-nir) *Norse* Odin's eight-legged horse, which Hermod rode into the underworld to reclaim his dead brother, Baldur.

SUSANO-O (soo-**sah**-noh-oh) *Japanese* The god of storms.

TARANGA (**tah**-rahn-gah) *Polynesian* The mother of Maui.

TARENYAWAGO (**tar**-en-**ya**-wah-go) *Iroquois/Native American* The keeper of the heavens who forms the Iroquois confederacy, and who promotes peace and lives on earth as Hiawatha.

TARTARUS (**tar**-tah-rus) *Greek/Roman* The underworld.

TEFNUT (**teff**-noot) *Egyptian* The goddess of dew and moisture.

TEZCATLIPOCA (**tez**-caht-**lee**-poh-ka) *Mexican* A trickster god who helps and opposes mortals and Quetzalcoatl.

THOR (**thor**) *Norse* The god of thunder.

THOTH (**toth**) *Egyptian* The god of writing, logic, and judgment.

THRYM (**thrim**) *Norse* A giant and a master thief who steals Thor's hammer.

TIAMAT (**tee**-ah-maht) *Babylonian* See Apsu.

TITANS (**tie**-tuhns) *Greek* The race of giants, created from the union of Gaia and Uranus, that precedes the gods.

TSUKIYOMI (soo-kee-**yoh**-mee) *Japanese* The god of the moon.

UKEMOCHI (**you**-kee-moh-chee) *Japanese* The goddess of food.

UNKULUNKULU (un-koo-**lun**-koo-loo) *Zulu/African* The supreme being.

URANUS (you-**ray**-nus) *Greek* The personification of the heavens who is the son and husband of Gaia.

UTNAPISHTIM (oot-**nah**-pish-tim) *Babylonian* A mortal whom the gods instruct to build an ark for the great flood and later grant immortality.

VALHALLA (**val**-hal-lah) *Norse* Odin's palace in Asgard (heaven), which he shares with slain heroes.

VALKYRIES (val-**kye**-reez) *Norse* Odin's beautiful maidens, who fly horses onto battlefields and carry dead heroes to Valhalla. Literally, "choosers of the slain."

VE (**vee**) *Norse* One of Odin's brothers who helps to destroy the frost giants.

VENUS (**vee**-nus) *Roman* See Aphrodite.

VIGRID (**vih**-grid) *Norse* The field on which the final battle of the gods will be played out.

VILI (**vee**-lee) *Norse* One of Odin's brothers who helps to destroy the frost giants.

VULCAN (**vul**-cahn) *Roman* See Hephaestus.

YAMA (**yah**-ma) *Hindu* The god of the dead and the master of the underworld who is also the first man to be created and the first to die.

YMIR (**ee**-meer) *Norse* The first living creature, a frost giant born of fire and ice, and from whose body the earth is created.

YOMI (**yoh**-mee) *Japanese* The underworld.

YU HUANG (**you hoo**-ahng) *Chinese* The supreme god and master of heaven, who is also known as the Jade Emperor.

ZEUS (**zyoos**) *Greek* The first of the gods, who defeats the Titans and becomes king of the gods. Called Jupiter by the Romans.

SUGGESTED READING

Andersen, Johannes C. *Myths and Legends of the Polynesians.* Mineola, New York: Dover Publications, 1995.

Arnott, Kathleen. *African Myths and Legends.* New York: Oxford University Press, 1990.

Bulfinch, Thomas. *The Age of Chivalry and the Legends of Charlemagne.* New York: Marboro Books, 1992.

———. *The Age of Fable.* Philadelphia: Running Press, 1990.

Campbell, Joseph. *The Hero with a Thousand Faces.* Princeton: Princeton University Press, 1990.

Campbell, Joseph, with Bill Moyers. *The Power of Myth.* New York: Doubleday, 1988.

Coomaraswamy, Ananda K., and Sister Nivedita *Myths of the Hindus and Buddhists.* Mineola, New York: Dover Publications, 1967.

Crossley-Holland, Kevin. *The Norse Myths.* New York: Pantheon Books, 1981.

Eliot, Alexander. *The Universal Myths.* New York: Dutton Books, 1990.

Erdoes, Richard, and Alfonso Ortiz, editors. *American Indian Myths and Legends.* New York: Pantheon Books, 1985.

Graves, Robert. *The Greek Myths.* Mt. Kisco, New York: Moyer Bell, 1988.

Hamilton, Edith. *Mythology.* New York: Dutton, 1989.

Leeming, David Adams. *The World of Myth.* New York: Oxford University Press, 1991.

Lowie, Robert H. *Myths and Traditions of the Crow Indians.* Lincoln, Nebraska: University of Nebraska Press, 1993.

Mackenzie, Donald A. *Myths of China and Japan*. Avenel, New Jersey: Gramercy Books, 1994.

———. *Myths and Legends of India*. Mineola, New York: Dover Publications, 1989.

Mercatante, Anthony. *The Facts on File Encyclopedia of World Mythology and Legend*. New York: Facts on File, 1988.

Radin, Paul, editor. *African Folktales*. New York: Schocken Books, 1987.

Rolleston, T. W. *Celtic Myths and Legends*. Mineola, New York: Dover Publications, 1990.

Rosenberg, Donna. *World Mythology*, 2nd ed., Chicago: National Textbook Company, 1993.

Sandars, N. K., translator. *The Epic of Gilgamesh*. New York: Penguin Books, 1960.

Spence, Lewis. *Myths of the North American Indians*. Avenel, New Jersey: Gramercy Books, 1994.

Sproul, Barbara C. *Primal Myths*. San Francisco: HarperSanFrancisco, 1979.

Van Over, Raymond, editor. *Sun Songs: Creation Myths from Around the World*. New York: Dutton, 1980.

Werner, E. T. *Myths and Legends of China*. Mineola, New York: Dover Publications, 1994.

ABOUT THE AUTHOR

Steven Zorn has written on many subjects, ranging from computers to kissing. His books include *Masterpieces*, a coloring-book introduction to fine art, and retellings of Aesop's fables, Greek myths, American folktales, and Victorian ghost stories.

Raised in Albany, New York, Zorn studied at SUNY/Buffalo and Temple University. Currently associate producer of the award-winning television documentary series *Archaeology*, he resides in Virginia Beach, Virginia. *A World of Myths and Legends* is his eleventh book.